THE REFLECTIVE JOURNEY

A Practitioner's Guide to the Low Arousal Approach

by

Professor Andrew McDonnell

BSc, MSc, PhD

Clinical Psychologist

CEO, Studio3

Visiting Professor of Autism Studies

Birmingham City University

Published by Studio3

Printed by Book Printing UK www.bookprintinguk.com

Remus House, Coltsfoot Drive, Peterborough, PE2 9BF

Printed in Great Britain

ISBN 978-1-9160981-0-7

ACKNOWLEDGEMENTS

I would like to thank my wife Denise, as well as my longstanding Studio3 colleagues and fellow passengers on the low arousal journey. Like all journeys, the observations of my fellow travellers have helped me to understand my experiences along the way. As for practitioners, there are so many from the UK, Ireland and Scandinavia that the list of thanks would be never-ending. To all of my colleagues, you know you have my eternal gratitude. Particular mention should be made of Rachel McDermott for her editorial contributions, and Sean Macreavy for his photography and artistic support, with assistance from Chris Scully, Jade Gisbourne and Louis Hempell. Many thanks to the Hempell family and Alex Shinnick for participating as models. I also want to acknowledge the recent sad passing of Dr. Michael McCreadie, a true friend with a wonderful mind, who would always seek clarity in my thinking. I dedicate this book to him as a fellow 'journeyman' and practitioner of the low arousal approach.

A PHILOSOPHICAL THOUGHT

'"From caring comes courage." We might add that from it also comes wisdom. It's rather significant, we think, that those who have no compassion have no wisdom. Knowledge, yes; cleverness, maybe; wisdom, no.'

-       *The Tao of Pooh* by Benjamin Hoff (1982) p.128

Contents

FOREWORD

Managing behaviours can be extremely distressing for carers. We have all experienced scary and sometimes highly emotional situations when a person is experiencing what we would now describe as a 'meltdown'. This can occur in people's homes and a range of different settings. If there is a simple message for practitioners, it is that we can get much better at managing these situations. The key to all of this is that we develop our skills after experiencing a high arousal situation by examining our own behaviour first, and then learning and reflecting on how we can improve next time. I call this a Low Arousal Approach to managing behaviours.

Non-confrontational approaches are not a new idea. The roots of humanism can be found in a whole range of different philosophies. Many religious approaches espouse the 'Do No Harm' principle. Whilst there are many leading Buddhist, Christian and philosophers of other religions, the shared belief is that punishment-based approaches are not the best way forward. To give an example, the educator and children's author Janusz Korczak believed that all forms of corporal punishment were wrong because they did not educate children (Korczak died in Auschwitz in 1942). When we are supporting people who are often vulnerable and distressed, these same principles should be applied to any good form of crisis management.

Low arousal approaches mostly focus on the management of difficult behaviours in care settings. The first use of the term was in the early 1990's (McDonnell, McEvoy and Dearden, 1994). Since this time, there have been many publications that have focused on this subject.

THE REFLECTIVE JOURNEY

My colleagues Linda Woodcock and Andrea Page wrote a book called *Managing Family Meltdown: The Low Arousal Approach and Autism* (Woodcock and Page, 2009). Bo Hejlskov Elvén, my colleague in Scandinavia, wrote a practitioner book called *No Fighting, No Biting, No Screaming: How to Make Behaving Positively Possible for People with Autism and Other Developmental Disabilities* (Hejlskov Elvén, 2010). My own book, *Managing Aggressive Behaviour in Care Settings: Understanding and Applying Low Arousal Approaches*, described the approach and how to apply it to a range of care settings (McDonnell, 2010).

Over the last twenty-five years, low arousal approaches have become increasingly popular within organisations in a large number of countries. This manual has been developed after repeated requests from colleagues and practitioners for a 'simple guide' for the everyday practitioner. Therefore, this manual has much more of a practitioner focus, and it is hoped that the reader should be able to understand and apply a low arousal approach by the end of this series of simple steps.

My Own Low Arousal Journey

To understand how this approach has developed, it is useful to provide the reader with information about how the approach grew from a personal point of view. I first became interested in the concept of arousal and its regulation when I was working in institutionalised care environments in the UK in the early 1980's. As a young psychology graduate, I wanted to change the world and 'make a difference'. I was delighted when I was offered a job as a support worker in a specialist day service for adults with intellectual disabilities who had what was described then as 'behaviour

2

problems'. I learned so much from entering this strange new world where responses to crisis were viewed as everyday occurrences. I remember a member of staff telling me, "We work with the worst here". The explosiveness of crisis situations was often punctuated with periods of intense boredom - for both staff and service users. I observed that individuals with physical and intellectual disabilities did often 'appear' to become aggressive, but it seemed clear to me even at an early age that violence is interactive. Many staff members appeared to increase states of physiological arousal often by raising their voices or invading people's space. In many situations, these individuals seemed to be oblivious to their own contribution towards challenging situations. I want to be clear that I was asked to implement some programmes that had strong punishment-based elements. Even now, all these years later, I still wonder why I did not question some of the practices at the time.

In contrast, there were some people who seemed to not trigger behaviours. It also became clear to me that these individuals often exuded a sense of calm in crisis situations with distressed individuals. I remember working with a woman named Jane who had autism, whom I was told by colleagues to 'watch carefully' and to be on guard because she 'likes to pull hair'. I remember thinking, 'No wonder this job was easy to get'. Later, I found out that I was the only candidate for the interview, and that they liked me based on the fact that I had studied martial arts. I was working directly with her, seated beside her at a table. To me, she seemed to be enjoying our table-top game. When I explained to her that the session had to finish, her face changed. She went very red, stared at me and grabbed my hair with both hands saying "NO!" I then found myself with my head being pressed down on the table.

The pain was so intense that at first, I froze. She did not shout, but continued to hold me in a vice-like grip. I became aware that my colleague Peter had entered the room. He was an experienced care worker who always walked with a 'bubble of calmness' around him. He had quickly taken me under his wing when I first started working there. I had been told that this was one of the best services for supporting people who were very challenging. We used punitive methods 'when required', and (even for its time in the 1980's) the establishment was well known for adopting a rigid, consequence-based approach. Where today we would see these individuals as distressed and traumatised with arousal regulation issues, back then individuals with behaviours of concern were viewed with far less empathy.

I began to really feel the pain in the roots of my hair (presumably my beta-endorphins - the body's natural pain killers - had begun to wear off). I shouted at her (as I had been taught in the 80s) in the most masterful voice I could muster: "Jane you are being a silly girl! Let go of Andy's hair now!" The immediate effect was that she pulled down even harder. When I repeated the request, the same thing happened again. Later in my career, I would understand that staying calm was vital in such situations. However, as my arousal level increased, my anger turned to panic. I started to shout at my colleague, "Peter, mate, get her off me!", blissfully unaware that the louder I shouted the harder she pulled my hair.

That's when I heard the phrase that truly changed my perspective, and started me on my journey of non-confrontation. Very calmly, Peter replied, "Andy, stop shouting. You're scaring Jane". I was stunned into silence. He told me to breathe, relax, and then gently touched Jane's arms and told her, "You are hurting Andy, and Andy is nice". He asked her if she wanted him to sit with her and she finally let go of my hair. As he sat down, he looked at me smiling and said, "I could do with a cup of tea".

As I walked away, I heard Jane mutter, "Sorry Andy", but at the time I was angry with her and struggled to accept her apology. When I had time to think about it over the next few days, however, I found that it was difficult to remain angry. On the other hand, it was easy to recognise her as a complex individual who was developmentally young. Following an incident, we were always given time to compose ourselves and de-brief, as well as being asked write up an ABC (Antecedent, Behaviour, Consequence) Chart Form. These protocols were definitely helpful, and considered 'cutting edge' for their time. Looking back, this period of reflection was one of the best aspects of the system. As I reflected on the incident with Jane, I found myself feeling a little embarrassed. It occurred to me that in my panic I had forgotten I was a martial arts expert, and hadn't recalled any of the moves and techniques that I could have used to break free from her. But it was not just blind panic that stopped me dead in my tracks. No, it was a realisation that a violent response would not help her. I had no wish to inflict pain on this vulnerable woman. In fact, the more I thought about it, the more I realised that in all the self-defence training I had experienced, the phrase 'mind over matter' was used often. This was usually paraphrased to 'your safety comes first'. However, whilst these principles may apply to a person who is attacked in a dark alley by a stranger, this was a young woman who I was paid to support. I vowed to myself then that I would never use physical techniques on the vulnerable, no matter how well I rationalised the situation.

Peter came to me after the incident for tea and a chat, and we discussed what I should do the next time a similar incident occurred. Peter's advice was amazing, and throughout the remainder of my time there he continued to teach me about what I now call a low arousal approach. The more he spoke and we reflected on what I had learned from the encounter with Jane, I started to experience something strange. What was this feeling? It was shame, mixed in with a little bit of guilt for good measure. How could I have shouted at her? How could that have helped? Obviously it was scary for Jane. Then, Peter said the thing I was dreading. "Andy, it's up to you how you go forward from here, but you shouldn't let people see that you're scared. I also think it is really important that you show Jane that there are no hard feelings". I went back into the room and said, "Does Jane want to play a game with Andy?" She smiled so sweetly that she melted my heart, causing another surge of vintage, high quality shame to wash over me like an ocean wave. I looked at her and said "Jane, Andy is sorry for shouting".

It took me years to reflect on these early experiences. I learned so much, especially from Peter, who was essentially from the University of Life – no First Class Honours in Psychology to be seen. Peter passed away a number of years ago, and I still regret that I never saw him after I left that job. My time there was short, but thanks to him it was a highly educational year. My key take-away from that role was that arousal is contagious, and that my personal responses affected Jane, and would continue to affect any other individual I supported. I learned so much from Peter, and greatly respect the unconditional degree of compassion and empathy he repeatedly showed to the people we supported. Most of all, he was just so calm.

I spent a year working in an institution for people with intellectual disabilities. Most of the people they asked me to support had highly traumatised histories. The wards (definitely not homes) were overcrowded, and in some ways, it felt more like a prison. I worked with some amazingly caring staff, but there were others who were just disconnected from the people they supported. I learned to recognise a small minority of people who seemed to enjoy demonstrating their power. My first debates with staff involved giving people cups of tea 'off the schedule'. I witnessed physical restraints being applied to people and it became clear to me that the largest cause of 'challenging behaviours' were the people supporting these individuals. It took me a long time to realise that these extreme experiences were going to shape my entire career. After leaving that place and training to be a Clinical Psychologist at the University of Birmingham, I began to realise that the responses to people in crises needed to be understood. I had by this time become a senior instructor in the martial art of Jiu Jitsu. One of my mentors was a no-nonsense Yorkshireman called Steve. He had amazing charisma and an in-depth understanding of what he often described as 'movement and emotion'. I also realised that I kept my world of psychology very separate from the world of martial arts. I attended many workshops at this time, often with titles that make me cringe today; 'Managing the Violent Patient' or, even worse, 'Aggression Management Training'. Most of the training had little theoretical rationale and consisted of learning physical self-defence strategies on gym mats, and I did not believe that they had any place in a caring environment. Ultimately, I decided to take a clean slate approach to training. This led to the founding of my organisation Studio3 in 1992. This is now an international training and consulting organisation with a strong focus on treating people with dignity and respect. I completed my

PhD in 2004 on the very subject of staff training in the management of challenging behaviours. Today my interests have expanded to include understanding stress responses, engaging people positively and, of course, an interest in the world of people with autism. I now work with colleagues all over the world, and alongside new collaborations and friendships have spawned new concepts. With a true friend and colleague Michael a McCreadie, I helped develop a stress management approach called the Atlass Programme.

It's been over 30 years since I left that first job and pursued my interest in training people to respond calmly in crisis situations. Since then, I have learned that regulating emotional arousal is at the heart of many so-called 'behavioural issues'. There is a positive message to good crisis management, and it is that the less fearful you are of a person, the more likely you are to support them in a positive manner. Once we learn to manage the behaviour of the people we support in a humane and effective manner, crisis management can become more of a science. It can also create the 'space' needed to develop meaningful relationships with people.

How To Use This Book

This book is for practitioners who support stressed and traumatised people with arousal regulation issues. It is my hope that it will be of interest to a wide range of professionals, and encourage them to reflect on their work. Throughout the book, I will use the term 'arousal regulation', as I dislike negative terminology such as 'de-regulation'. Understanding and regulating arousal has many generalised benefits, including increased learning and better health outcomes. The concept has a natural overlap with concepts such as

Mindfulness, which similarly seeks to reduce stress and encourage emotional regulation.

This book should be used as a guide by anyone supporting individuals who can become distressed. There are three ways to use this book most effectively. The first involves sequentially working through the chapters and then completing all of the worked examples. Any individual can adopt this approach. The second approach is to identify a group of individuals to work through these chapters sequentially and discuss the concepts. The third way is for an individual or group of people to identify specific areas that are relevant to their current experiences, such as working through the 'Control' chapter with a staff team who are a little too controlling, or looking at the 'Empathy' chapter with an individual or group who struggles to empathise with a distressed individual. Use this book as guide to help give you clear ideas for supporting people who are highly distressed.

So, what is this book going to be about? I am going to attempt to explain why arousal regulation is so important in supporting people. The examples I will use will be from a broad range of areas, all real-life experiences of my own and my colleagues. For me, the journey I am on has been exciting and rewarding, and it is my hope that this book will provide an honest framework for supporting people. I have called this book *The Reflective Journey* as it is so important to be aware of our own behaviour in order to truly support people in crisis. Enjoy the journey.

Professor Andrew McDonnell, 2019

PART ONE: LOOKING WITHIN

CHAPTER 1

UNDERSTANDING DISTRESSED BEHAVIOURS

Whether we are at home or work, we will experience aggressive behaviour at some point in our careers. It can be very distressing to experience these behaviours. The relationship we have with the individual person is always important. Think about arguments you may have had with a family member, close friend, or even a dispute with a stranger. The context (who, when, where, why) really does have a big impact. This book will mostly focus on how to manage these behaviours, but in order to do that it is also important to think about a simple approach to understanding these behaviours.

We struggle to explain our own behaviours on a day-to-day basis. Think of the number of times that you have struggled to understand why you might have done something. For some people, they may buy something they do not necessarily need, or become argumentative over what appears to be a trivial subject. The reality is that we often try to understand our own behaviour, especially if we are stressed. Understanding the behaviour of someone you are supporting can also be very confusing. We may see someone behaving bizarrely and, despite our best efforts, have no explanation for what they might be doing.

To explain behaviours, we have to examine the reasons why we think behaviours occur, and this involves analysing our own framework of understanding. There are many different schools of thought in Psychology, ranging from the Psychodynamic models in which many behaviours are learnt in childhood and therefore almost impossible to change in adulthood, to behavioural approaches which state that any behaviour which has been learnt can be unlearnt. There are still huge debates between competing schools of thought, and of course many individuals like myself combine different parts of each model. I would describe my personal approach as eclectic, adopting a view of the world that combines a multitude of different approaches. We may try to understand behaviour in terms of attachment, loss and trauma. At other times, we may focus more on the 'here and now' and be quite goal-orientated with a person. In some situations, we may experience a behaviour where there is a clear and obvious external trigger, such as a child screaming and shouting after her parents have said, "You have had enough sweets". Other times, the trigger may be less clear, and the parent wonders, "Why is my child behaving in this way?" In those situations, it may be that the child is highly stressed for a whole range of reasons which, as we will explore later in the book, can have a huge impact on behaviour. The most important thing to remember is that people are complex and live in a very complex world, therefore solutions may also require a complex response. The bad news is that, despite what people tell you, behaviour is not as simple as ABC.

Understanding Our Own Reactions to Behaviour

Our emotions are also challenged when we experience distressed behaviour. It is really important that people learn to separate their own feelings and emotions from those of the people they support. However, it is less obvious that behaviours can also have an impact on ourselves, as shown in the below example:

'Eve has been a support worker for people with Alzheimer's for over 10 years. She has worked with a range of extreme behaviours, but always tells her colleagues that she has 'gotten used to things'. The reality is that she is becoming more stressed as the years progress, and has developed a number of gastric complaints which she does not believe are connected to her job. Upon seeing a therapist, she is now beginning to understand that maybe her work is more stressful than she had first thought, and that 'bottling-up' her emotions was a bad idea.'

In Eve's case, she did not recognise and accept the added effect of day-to-day stressors on her life. It may well be that deep down she realised that she was starting to struggle with her work: however, the reality is that she probably did not connect her own behaviour with the behaviour of the people she supported. Understanding the emotional consequences of our work is so important, and the earlier we can learn to identify stressors and tune in to our own bodies and minds, the better.

Most of this book will be about good and effective behaviour management. Trying to understand behaviours is essential if we are to stop constantly moving from one crisis to another. There is a constant message that behaviour is 'not as simple as ABC'; rather, that it is complex and determined by many different factors. Physicists spend their entire careers trying to understand how the universe works. To this day, they still struggle to explain basic processes in physics such as time. In the quantum world, even the prediction of objects is uncertain. When we start to think about human behaviour, there is a clear word of caution; simple explanations will not get us very far in the process. To give you a good example of the complexities of understanding human behaviour, just consider how we understand the weather. At present we cannot fully predict weather patterns as we simply do not have knowledge of all the variables and factors which affect the weather. Nonetheless, we can predict weather patterns to a reasonable degree of certainty. We can say that it is likely to rain next week, but we may not be able to predict with a high degree of certainty that it will rain at two o'clock in the afternoon on a specific day. The reality is that the weather is a chaotic system, and this means that our ability to predict patterns of weather only goes so far. Of course it is useful to predict weather patterns, but we need to accept when we have reached the limits of our understanding. The same goes for understanding and predicting behaviour.

The language we use to describe behaviours and situations that may be distressing is very important. We readily use terms such as 'violence', 'aggression', and 'tantrums'. These words impact on the stereotypes we have about people. For example, if you call someone 'violent', you will often make the assumption that they are by extension a 'violent person'. Even phrases that seem quite neutral can be overused. For example, when we say that a person is using a behaviour 'to get attention'. Attention is a very value-laden term; to many people it implies that a behaviour is wilful and deliberate. In extreme situations, people may refer to individuals as 'manipulative'. Thinking that someone is 'manipulating' you or your friends and colleagues will only lead to a negative view of that person, as well as implying that they are acting with malicious intent and are therefore in control of their actions. The psychologist Ross Greene, in his book *The Explosive Child* (1998), argues that children are often trying to do their best despite behaving badly. If the language we use implies that they are bad, they will start to believe it themselves. Therefore, it is important to think about the way we describe behaviours to our friends and colleagues, and the implications those descriptions have. The neutral term that is most commonly used to describe these behaviours while avoiding negative assumptions is 'behaviours of concern'.

Defining Behaviours of Concern

Psychologist Eric Emerson defines behaviour of concern in his book *Challenging Behaviour: Analysis and Intervention in People with Severe Intellectual Disabilities* (1995) as:

> '*A culturally abnormal behaviour of such intensity, frequency or duration that the physical safety of the person or others is likely to be placed in serious jeopardy, or behaviour that is likely to seriously limit the use of, or result in the person being denied access to, ordinary community facilities.*'

This definition is useful because it does not just look at behaviours which are physically challenging, but also those which could be seen as socially unacceptable or stressful for others.

Let us consider three examples:

Example 1: Julie has difficulty coping with bright lights and also reacts very strongly when she hears a baby crying. She has kicked and bitten her parents when she is in a situation she finds difficult. Her parents are worried about taking her into public places in case they see a family with a baby.

Example 2: Sean has pica, an eating disorder which means that he picks up anything on the floor and puts it in his mouth. He also makes loud noises when he is excited and will run up to people and look in their pockets for handkerchiefs. His family find it really difficult to go out in a public place with Sean as they get very embarrassed when he approaches strangers, and when people turn to look at him when he makes a noise.

Example 3: James is an adolescent with a history of trauma. He can be described as 'stubborn'. His social worker regularly agrees a behavioural contract with him that is supposed to be binding agreement. In reality, he does not follow rules set by other people.

All of these situations fit in with Emerson's definition in that the behaviours are discouraging people from giving these individuals access to facilities in the community and preventing them from enjoying what I would describe as a 'normal life'. In Julie's case, there is also the problem of her physically aggressive behaviours which may be putting her or others' physical safety at risk. Intensity, frequency and duration are also identified by Emerson as key factors in considering behaviours as challenging.

There are a number of factors that affect how carers view behaviours of concern. Their personal experience of the behaviour, how they feel about that behaviour and how others react to it are all factors that can make it seem more intense to one person than it perhaps would to someone else. If the behaviour has increased in frequency, people may feel alarmed and concerned. In other situations, a behaviour may be low in frequency, but when it does occur, is extremely intense. Low frequency and high intensity behaviours can often be the most difficult to manage, especially if there is some kind of predictable pattern. For example:

'Charlie is an adult with a history of alcohol abuse and violence directed towards the people who have been supporting him over the years. He has been in a rehabilitation programme, and most of the staff report that he is 'a changed person'. Despite the progress, Charlie will still lose his temper, and when he does, it usually takes him at least 30 minutes to calm down. His behaviours have reduced from weekly occurrences to monthly, and the trend is downward. It is difficult for some staff to cope with this change and, although they are in the minority, many state that they feel his behaviour is getting worse despite the evidence to the contrary.'

In Charlie's example, his support staff have had little experience of and exposure to his anger. When it does occur, they are almost unprepared emotionally. Understanding that he is actually progressing is a crucial part of the problem. The reality is that his verbal aggression has become more intense and lower in frequency, but his property destruction and physical violence has all-but disappeared. How we evaluate evidence is really important when we think about day-to-day behaviours.

Despite our search for objective measures of people's behaviours, we are reliant on our own worldview. To a certain degree, all observations are 'theory-laden', meaning that a great deal depends on your own perspective. Einstein (1927) argued that observation was necessary but essentially flawed in a simple example that described a beach ball being thrown from a moving train. He argued that three different observers (positioned in front, behind and at 90 degrees) could witness the same beach ball being thrown from the train, but their observations would depend on their perspective. This principle can be applied to our day-to-day interactions with the people we support. Practitioners are often expected to record and describe behaviours in care and support work. Sometimes, two people can describe their experiences very differently. Understanding that observations are inextricably linked to a single perspective can mean that sometimes we have to accept that two observations may both be correct - especially in fearful situations. The famous psychologist Albert Bandura said that 'all behaviour is about perception', and this certainly applies to behaviours of concern (1977).

Our Own Tolerance Levels

If the behaviours identified as challenging are occurring frequently, then carers are more likely to feel worn down and be less tolerant of them. Acknowledgement of tolerance levels is important since how carers mentally cope with a behaviour will determine how they approach it. Many things can affect our tolerance levels. Look at the following factors listed below:

Tiredness, context, physical environment/culture, support of colleagues and significant others, our values and beliefs, our previous experiences of distressed behaviours, our relationship with the person, our own stress and physical health.

THE REFLECTIVE JOURNEY

Think about how these factors might affect you in different situations. Now, try to rate the following behaviours in terms of your own tolerance. When doing this exercise, it is important that you do it quickly and try not to overthink your answers. It is also really important that you try to be as honest as you can. This is a five=point scale, ranging from 1 (easily tolerable) to 5 (absolutely intolerable).

Factor/ rating	Easily Tolerable 1	Tolerable 2	Not sure 3	Slightly Intolerable 4	Absolutely Intolerable 5
I am very tired.					
The behaviour occurs in a public setting.					
The behaviour occurs in your own home.					
The environment is physically overcrowded.					
Lack of support from colleagues and significant others.					

The person has a high degree of control over their behaviour.					
The person is in a position of authority i.e. a police officer.					
The person has consumed alcohol.					
You know and like the person.					
Swearing.					
The person verbally threatens you.					
The person breaks property.					

The person throws an object at you.					
The person cuts themselves.					
The person threatens you with a knife.					
You are working on your own.					
Your stress levels are very high.					
You have a migraine or similar health issue.					
The person has strong body odour.					

Which of these factors did you rate as most affecting your tolerance level? (consider the 4's and 5's). Think about how much your behaviour is affected by relatively simple things. One of the most simple factors is your own physical health. You may have days where you feel 'under the weather', and in these circumstances you will find it more difficult to tolerate these behaviours. One of the most common behaviours that people rate as easy to tolerate is swearing, but this is not always the case. Look at the following example:

*'Callum is a twelve-year-old boy with multiple diagnoses of ADHD, Autism, and Tourette's Syndrome. His parents love him very much, but they find that when he is excited, and especially in public places, he will swear for long periods of time. On a train journey, he once told an elderly couple to "**** off". The elderly couple were very distressed, and his parents were extremely embarrassed. Callum laughed out loud as he shouted the 'bad words'. As the swearing continued, his parents decided to move to another seat on the train. They have noticed over the years that the more they ask him to stop, the more he tends to swear.'*

Embarrassment is a huge factor when considering our tolerances. In the above example, Callum's parents have no simple answer to managing their young boy's behaviour. They have become tolerant to his swearing because they rightly see it as stress-related and compulsive. It is difficult for other people to view his behaviour as anything but rude and, in some cases, even attention-seeking. If you ranked swearing lowly when evaluating your own tolerances, ask yourself honestly, is that truly the case?

Stress and tiredness are also important to consider. The more tired we are, the less tolerant we become. Similarly, our own stress levels have a huge part to play, as does the social context of where the behaviour takes place. For example, is the behaviour occurring at home or in a public place? In my experience, people often feel shame and guilt if somebody is shouting or swearing at them in a public area. In these situations, there can be a strong urge to respond to these behaviours. Our relationship with the person is also very important. Do we like them? It is really difficult to tolerate distressed behaviour from someone whom you struggle to like or fail to have an empathic understanding of.

Our own past experiences and 'world view' can also affect our behaviour and reactions. To give a real-life example, consider the following:

'John is a twenty-five-year-old adult male. He is a specialist youth worker, working with the most traumatised adolescents. In his own adolescence, John himself lived in care homes where he had a wide range of negative experiences. He was also the victim of excessive restraint by some of his carers.'

In the above example, John's past experiences have made him a very caring, empathic young man who can identify with the support needs of the young people he works with. John is extremely against using of any form of physical restraint, a view which has come about from a learned experience. His life experiences have made him both a resilient and an effective practitioner. In the next example we see an alternative world view:

'Felicity is a twenty-eight-year-old mother of two children who works in a youth setting. In the past, she was a victim of marital

abuse, which she feels she has now 'come to terms with'. She routinely hears young people using offensive language, which deeply distresses her. She often gently challenges the children, but their behaviour just seems to continue. Felicity is becoming increasingly frustrated and distressed that the children she supports are not listening to her and following her instructions.'

Felicity is someone who is trying to work positively with the young children, but struggles with verbally threatening abusive behaviour, especially from males. She has been very open and honest with her colleagues about these issues and accepts that she has a problem with this specific type of behaviour. Felicity is also aware that her previous history of marital abuse has impacted her tolerance to behaviours. In this example, Felicity is a highly reflective person who, by acknowledging a problem with tolerance, can be supported by her colleagues. We are all aware that it is difficult not to personalise behaviours, and in Felicity's case she attempted to overcome this by being aware of the issue and taking practical steps to seek support from her colleagues.

Some Common Causes of Behaviours of Concern

We have acknowledged that behaviour is complex, and that there are many factors which we cannot always understand and predict (just like the weather). Schopler and Mesibov (1994) use the 'tip of the Iceberg' approach, such that what is seen above sea level is the behaviour of concern, but what is

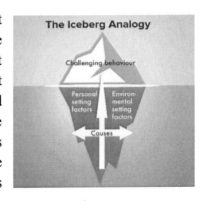

23

hidden below sea level is what really needs to be tackled – the underlying causes of the visible behaviours (e.g. communication difficulties, sensory issues etc).

There is no single cause of behaviours of concern, and the complexity of behaviour as a whole means that it not always easy or possible to establish a cause every time. However, there are some causes which are fairly common and should always be considered:

Physical Health - Whenever behaviour takes a turn for the worse, it is important to begin by checking the person's physical health. If we are stressed, we are statistically far more likely to experience everyday minor illnesses (Yaribeygi et al., 2017). One of the most obvious factors to consider is whether a person is experiencing pain, or something similar to pain. Many individuals struggle to communicate that they are in pain, and in some circumstances do not appear to identify an experience as being painful. Pain is often confused with emotional distress. A recent series of studies in the United States have found that even so-called 'everyday' pain relieving drugs, such as Tylenol, may be dampening down emotional responsivity (Durso et al., 2015). Another study showed that the common UK painkiller paracetamol reduces empathy in response to others' pain (Mischkowski, Crocker and Way, 2016).

In a recent UK review, Sir Geoffry Marmot concluded that people with disabilities have poorer health outcomes than the rest of the population (2017). In my experience, good health screening is often recommended by professionals, but rarely happens in practice. There are many everyday illnesses that people who are highly stressed are more susceptible to, such as gastric problems, migraines, other pain-related conditions (for example Fibromyalgia, Crohn's disease,

Irritable Bowel Syndrome and Chronic Fatigue conditions). The worst thing to do in practice would be to focus on the behaviours of concern of someone who may be unwell, without a full understanding of their internal, physical and emotional world. It is also very important to remember that physical health issues apply as much to supporters and family members as they do to the person themselves.

Lack of Structure and Predictability - The more stressed people become, the more out of control they feel. Highly stressed people may view the world as being unpredictable and unstable. To make the world more predictable, people often attempt to simplify it. One way of doing this is for the person to isolate themselves from other people. On a day-to-day level, people may become more focused on rituals and routines in order to provide themselves with some form of structure. The opposite can also occur, whereby some people lose all sense of structure entirely. The reality of this situation is an individual whose life appears chaotic and focused on a 'here-and-now' mentality and 'moment-to-moment thinking'.

Predictability and stress are very closely related to one another. My Belgian colleague, Peter Vermeulen, maintains that unpredictability increases levels of stress (personal communication, 2019). The opposite of unpredictability is a predictable world where people can make sense of the apparent chaos. We need structure, routine and sameness to give people predictability. This is true not just for people on the Autism spectrum, but for a whole range of conditions where high degrees of stress is a major factor. For example, children and adults who have experienced some form of trauma or loss and people with a range of mental health issues often require structure to assist them on the road to recovery. It is also true that, to a certain degree, we all need structure and routine. Structure helps us to make sense of a chaotic world. For some people, having a daily visual schedule or making clear lists is very beneficial. Routines and rituals also encourage predictable and familiar moments in time. It is important to not always view rituals as negative in nature - they are often just coping strategies that a person needs to feel more stable.

Stress - People with high levels of stress or anxiety struggle to cope with even simple daily tasks and activities. Chronic stress can be a debilitating condition. It is true that some people work in circumstances that by their very nature can be highly stressful situations. Astronauts are good examples of individuals who have to be trained to cope with high degrees of stress. Good astronauts are people who thrive, somewhat literally, on pressure. Of course, the risk of harm is quite high, which is what makes the job so stressful.

For people who work in care settings or support loved ones, stress can be a constant companion. In these circumstances, it is important that we reduce stress as much as possible. By reducing the stress of both supporters and individuals, behaviours of concern will also be reduced (Rippon et al., 2019). Managing a person's stress and helping them to regulate their arousal levels can often be more beneficial than focusing on an individual or their behaviour. Stress is what we call transactional in nature, meaning that our stress affects other people and vice versa (Lazarus and Folkman, 1984). It is not uncommon for people to fail to notice how their own stress impacts on the stress levels of other people. My colleagues Professor Mark Wetherell, Michael Smith and Daniel Rippon from the Stress Research Group at the University of Northumbria, have been collaborating with my colleagues at Studio3 in examining carer stress and what we can do to combat it. Some of this research has reinforced the idea that many people are not fully aware of how stressed they are.

Sometimes the sources of work-based stress are surprising. My colleague Daniel Rippon, in a soon to be published study, interviewed staff who supported people with behaviours of concern about the things that make them feel stressed at work. He found that the behaviour of their colleagues was very high on this list, including things such as colleagues being 'lazy' or not following advice or guidance (Rippon et al., 2019). Stress is a core component of any behaviour management approach, and it is important that stress management is applied to all people concerned, not just the person exhibiting behaviours of concern. Many people support highly complex individuals in stressful situations with very little focus on their own stress management. A simple rule should always be to focus on managing your own stress first before you start focusing on a person you support.

Trauma - Past trauma can have a huge impact on behaviours. In some situations, exposure to extreme and sustained stress can lead to Post Traumatic Stress Disorder (PTSD). Anyone who experiences PTSD knows that the fear and panic experienced can be very debilitating. Much of the research on PTSD has involved many of the world's militaries. In the United States, one of the world's leading positive psychologists, Professor Martin Seligman from the University of Pennsylvania, has been involved in a project to foster resilience in US military personnel (Seligman, 2011). On a more positive note, with the right support, many people can recover from PTSD to a level where they are able to function in society. However, most trauma may not take the obvious form of battlefield trauma.

Trauma can also be transmitted to people. This is particularly true of people who care for others, especially if they are highly empathic people. Trauma can also be transmitted 'vicariously', meaning that someone's experience is lived through in the imagination of another. In care environments, it is not unusual for staff to talk about specific incidents that they found traumatising, and at the same time be unaware that they are transmitting a trauma-based message. Abuse can also cause trauma, which is sometimes difficult to spot as it can take many different forms. It can be very clear in terms of a trigger (as can be the case for physical or sexual abuse), or it can be more pervasive and difficult to spot, such as in the case of marital abuse. Trauma is a factor in many behaviours of concern. It is often misunderstood by practitioners who focus on very noticeable trauma that has clear life events as triggers. For some of the individuals we support, small everyday phenomena can lead to trauma. The following example demonstrates what we would describe as trauma which may not be noticed by individuals:

'Ethel is eighty-four years old and has a deteriorating form of dementia. When her husband visits her in her care home, her memories of the past are enhanced. The interactions between her and her husband are sometimes quite wonderful to witness. He has often said that when he talks about the past, he gets glimpses of the woman he first married. However, when her husband attempts to leave, she becomes very upset. The stress of seeing him depart is the same every day that he visits. Her husband is increasingly becoming more upset about visiting, but he knows that the visits are really important for both of them.'

In the above example, the staff who support Ethel view the visits as really positive, and to a certain degree, ignore the negative impact that the end of the visits have on both Ethel and her husband. It would perhaps be better if someone were to figure out a new way to end these sessions, or to increase their duration but reduce their frequency. Considering other options is essential to increase the quality time the pair spend together, and to reduce the trauma being caused by the departure of Ethel's husband.

Low-key trauma of this type is very common in a variety of situations. It can especially have a huge impact on very young children. Young babies will sometimes cry if their parents leave them or remove themselves from their child's line of sight. From the child's perspective, their mother may not be coming back as they are still trying to figure out how the world works. Similarly, many individuals who are developmentally young can experience the same loss and physical symptoms of stress when a familiar member of staff simply goes off duty. In care environments where there is high turnover of staff, many of the people who make strong bonds and connections with these individuals are then subjected to loss and trauma when they leave.

Sensory Overload - Many individuals who are highly stressed can experience sensory issues, and as a result they often develop behaviours which allow them to escape from situations they find intolerable. Sensory overload is often a side effect of increased stress. Sensory hyper-reactivity is not just something that occurs in one field, such as Autism. Any person who experiences an increase in their stress levels may be sensitive to sounds, smells, touch and tastes. For most people, reducing stress can have a big impact on these behaviours.

Traumatic memories can also have sensory component. I recall working with a Romanian orphan who had a diagnosis of Autism and attachment issues. As an adult, she struggled with the colour orange (orange is similar to the rusty colouring of the metal cots in her Romanian orphanage). Romanian folk music also seemed to be a trigger for behaviours of concern. However, let us not forget that sensory memories can also be positive. Most individuals reading this book will be able to identify a particular smell, food or experience that they have fond memories of from being a child. When you are reading this, think about tastes, smells and sounds from your childhood that remind you of pleasant thoughts and feelings. This is an example of how we can use our sensory memories to have a positive impact on our stress and well-being.

Slow Processing of Information - Like a computer, we all have a certain degree of mental processing power. We are constantly processing information through our senses and trying to sort this information out in our brains, rather like the sorting room in a post office. Unfortunately, recent research from neuroscientists shows that we do not just process information sequentially; we are also processing information from a range of sources at the same time. In his book *Thinking, Fast and Slow* (2011), Nobel Prize winning Psychologist Daniel Kahneman argues that there are two types of processes in the human brain, which he calls System 1 and System 2. System 1 is an automatic, fast and often unconscious way of thinking which requires little energy, but is prone to bias and error. System 2, on the other hand, is effortful, slow and controlled. My colleague, Peter Vermeulen, argues that our brains are constantly making predictions about what is going to happen now and next (personal communication, 2019). He believes that when information becomes confused we are unable to make clear predictions, which then leads to a heightened state of stress. To make matters slightly worse, we also know that increased stress and physiological arousal will lead to slower processing of information, which in turn will also increase our stress. This creates a 'vicious circle' whereby poor processing increases our stress levels, and as our stress levels increase, the poorer we process information. This is especially problematic for System 1 type of thinking where we would expect a person to make more biases and errors. For example, a person who is experiencing a mental health crisis may process information more slowly, as well as their cognitive biases fuelling their paranoid thinking.

Frustration - Many behaviours of concern are related to communication issues, and the frustration that people experience in attempting communicate with other people. Communication problems between carers and the person they support can often lead to frustration on both sides. Consider, for example, the frustration that some individuals with an acquired brain injury experience because they have a reduced ability to express their needs and wishes as rapidly as they did in the past. Similarly, frustration can occur when our time demands are not met. Think about the number of times you have been in a hurry (by the way, you should stop rushing) and you find you have to queue for a train or bus ticket. The queue is moving very slowly. Your frustration builds and builds, sometimes even leading to anger. It is amazing how often you will see people being blamed for events that they have little control over. In this example, blaming the ticket master or all the people in the queue for being slow will never help the situation, it will just increase your stress. In these circumstances, the angrier we become, the more we need a focus to vent our anger. Automated call services that keep you waiting for prolonged periods of time are another good example of everyday frustration. Even the phrase, 'Press 1 for X, 2 for Y and 9 to speak to a real live person' can cause stress levels to spike! The real danger lies in us not realising that our heightened emotional responses are contagious and can spread to others. In reality, we need to deal with our own frustration and accept that we can be part of the problem in these situations.

A Perceived Lack of Control Over Your Life

As a guiding rule, the more stressed you become, the more chaotic and unpredictable the world becomes. This will always produce negative coping strategies, which involve controlling the world around you or your immediate environment. People who are highly stressed may become extremely challenging if they feel that they are being threatened. Animal studies show us that controlling territory has survival value. In a controversial study, Professor Martin Seligman investigated a scenario in which a laboratory dog would receive an electric shock through the floor of a crate (Seligman, Maier and Geer, 1968). The dog was able to learn quickly that it could jump a small hurdle in a safe area and not be electrocuted. Seligman then electrified both sides of the crate. Some dogs continued jumping, but many just gave up despite being shocked. This he described as 'learned helplessness'. If you feel you can no longer control the outcomes, then it is more likely that you may give up. However, some of the animals did not give up, and this is important to understand when considering people who are highly distressed. The less in control the person believes themselves to be, the more they will fight to regain some form of control over other people. It is interesting to note that Professor Martin Seligman is now a leading influencer in positive psychology. Although cruel and clearly unethical, these early animal studies helped researchers to understand the importance of control in our lives.

I am reminded of a young woman who would provide instructions to people who entered her home. She would tell them, "Sit in that chair" or, my favourite, "Only speak to me if I ask you a question". This need for control is a common coping mechanism for any stressed person. A high perceived sense of control gives a person some sense of safety. Removing too much of that control will almost inevitably lead to behaviour of concern. Even more worrying is a growing wealth of research and literature which indicates that a low sense of perceived control can lead to poorer health outcomes.

Emotional Contagion

Emotions of all kinds can be contagious (Elvén, 2010). Sometimes behavioural triggers can involve a supporter being unaware that their anger or distress is being transmitted like a loud radio to the person they are supporting. Role modelling low mood to a person who is already depressed may actually make them even more miserable. Similarly, displaying positive emotions such as happiness may influence someone else's emotional state.

In one of the classic and most controversial deception studies in Psychology, students were given either a neutral vitamin injection or adrenaline (Schachter and Singer, 1962). The students were then allocated to a group exercise which contained planted actors who either modelled positive emotion (happiness) or negative emotion (anger). The people who had been given adrenaline reported being more happy or more angry than the others. There are a lot of debates about this and other studies, but it would appear that there are simple bodily processes which cause us to label our emotional state by considering both our internal and external world. When we are asked to work with someone who displays high levels of arousal, the emotion we convey to that person is really important. Therefore, appearing to be calm is just as important as maintaining calmness.

Lack of Empathy

The concept of having a lack of empathy is a potential cause of behaviour of concern. We sometimes talk of people lacking empathy or that ability to 'see through the eyes of others'. Empathy is a two-way street. My colleague, Damian Milton, who is an academic with an autism diagnosis, argues that many staff supporting people with autism lack an empathic understanding of the people they support. He calls this a 'double empathy problem' (Milton, 2012).

It is my opinion that a lack of empathic understanding will often lead to a negative view of that person's behaviour. We naturally try to alter this process ourselves by attempting to relate to other people's experiences. Think about the times when you have argued with a teenager, only to remind yourself that you were probably just as bad when you were their age. I should also stress that empathy is different from sympathy or pity. Empathy is the ability to connect with another person's feelings. Much of this book is based on developing a greater empathic understanding of people who can challenge us emotionally and even physically.

A False Belief That Behaviours are Intentional and Meant to Do You Harm

This concept is a little difficult for people to understand. How can my belief that a person is 'targeting me' be a potential cause of behaviours? The answer is relatively simple in nature. If you believe that you are being threatened you will naturally either avoid the person and situation, or you will confront and try to control that person to keep yourself safe. It is also more likely that you will personalise behaviours much more. It is really important to understand that, as human beings, we are constantly trying to figure out why a person behaves in the way they do. The more dangerous we perceive them to be, the less likely it is that we will want to help them. This can then lead to us behaving in a way that is actually more likely to increase the risk of meltdowns. In extreme cases, people can end up punishing people in the genuine belief that they will be able to change their behaviour.

Excessive Rules and Boundaries

We exist within a world that contains many rules we are expected to comply with. If you drive a car under the influence of alcohol and you are caught then there will be serious consequences. Rules can provide structure, but if there are too many boundaries surrounding a stressed person then this will most likely trigger challenging incidents. I often review support plans for stressed individuals who frequently experience 'meltdowns'. Within these, it is easy to find a number of statements that start with 'you should' or, 'you must'. The balance between having rules and boundaries as well as allowing freedom of expression will vary between individuals. Generally however, for highly stressed people, fewer rules and boundaries make the world a less stressful place.

Poor Attention and Memory

A common theme in care settings of all kinds is that sometimes we can forget that the person we are working with may have deficits in attention and memory. We often overestimate people's ability to understand simple tasks, and therefore it is easy to overwhelm people unintentionally. This is true for people with a wide range of labels from attention deficit hyperactivity disorder (ADHD), to autism, acquired brain injury, and schizophrenia. Attention can be thought of as a door that opens allowing you to walk through. Memory, both short and long term, is a process that changes over time. Our brains produce new connections into adulthood and beyond, but our short-term memory eventually declines. A short-term memory deficit may mean that you can remember a telephone number by repeating it to yourself out loud, but unless you repeat it a great deal you will forget the number very fast. Memory is complex and involves many different features. Memory for stories is different from facial memory (which is pretty robust in most people). Older people with dementia can often describe childhood memories in vivid detail but they cannot remember what they had for breakfast or the name of a new member of staff. As we get older, our deficits in short-term memory and other memory systems can become more pronounced (Park and Festini, 2017). Simple, everyday tasks can therefore become more and more challenging. Testing your ability to remember numbers can illustrate this point. Read this sequence of numbers out loud:

9 4 7 1 8 9 2 4 5 2

Look away for 5 seconds and see how many numbers you can remember. Most people will struggle to remember the full sequence the first time. Now, look at the sequence again and practice learning it. In 10 or 15 pages time, see if you are still able to recall the sequence correctly.

People – The largest cause of behaviour of concern is other people. We are interacting with people pretty much all of the time, especially if we are in a caring or support role. The vast majority of people are usually unaware that they trigger challenging incidents. Sadly, a small minority of people may wilfully and deliberately trigger behaviours. Thinking of ourselves as potential causes of behaviours of concern can have a significant impact. In my experience, far too often people view behaviours of concern as though they are observing fish in an aquarium. They are watching how these beings behave as detached observers. Many training programmes in behaviour support focus on the idea that we must be objective about behaviour. This is a really impressive aspiration, but the reality is that we are not observers – we are active participants in the change process. The positive message is that by altering our own behaviour, we may be able to reduce both our own stress and the stress level of the people we are supporting, thereby reducing instances of behaviour of concern.

Demands and Requests – One of the main causes of distressed behaviour is the individual being asked to do something by carers or family members. Research has shown that nearly two thirds of behaviours of concern were preceded by a demand or request from a carer (McDonnell, 2010). Demands and requests will often trigger meltdowns in people who are already hyperaroused and stressed. As both children and adults, we do not really like being told what we should and should not do. Some people are 'paradoxes', and often do the opposite when given instruction. I have often witnessed younger children not responding to requests to 'calm down', or the most useless of instructions - 'behave'. If demands and requests are reduced in times of crisis, behaviours of concern will be almost certainly be reduced. On the other hand, we cannot encourage individuals to go through life ignoring all demands and requests. Imagine going through passport control, being asked to produce your passport and replying, "No". How to gently make demands and requests to stressed people will be explored more closely later in this book.

Difficulties in Making a Connection With the Person

Maintaining positive relationships in western society is difficult. When we are working with someone who can be challenging, building a positive relationship can be a difficult process. People in care environments often develop relationships with supporters who ultimately leave them and move on with their careers. It is perhaps not surprising then that people who are stressed and traumatised often find it difficult to trust new supporters.

If you have difficulties developing a positive relationship with a person, this can potentially be a trigger for behaviours of concern. Sometimes, the chemistry is just not there between people. A colleague of mine who managed staff supporting very challenging people often used to say, "It's the staff who are the problem, not the clients!" This usually referred to a person who did not like the individual they supported, and vice versa. Often, incidents are triggered by a person not being trusted by an individual. In my early career, I was made a key worker for a very challenging young man who appeared to not like men. This young man was rarely challenging towards women, which begs the question of why a man was made his support worker in the first place. The obvious solution of having more women work with him was readily available. Sometimes we believe that people need to comply with our wishes, and clearly I was given this role because someone felt it was important to teach this young man to work with men. The major benefit I gained from the experience was improved cardiac fitness, as he spent many of our sessions chasing me around the room. When supporting people, it is important that we try to analyse the relationships that are working and why that is the case. We should always focus on positive relationships and building upon them. This is especially helpful when trying to provide a low arousal environment.

Can We Really Change Behaviours?

We are all prone to believing that we can change both our own and other people's behaviour. In the world of psychology, the debate about nature (our biology and genetics) and nurture (our learning environment) still resounds in our areas of work. The reality is that some 'hardwired' behaviours may not alter, whereas others could change. The key issue is to avoid the many extreme models. You can be a radical behaviourist, passionately believing that all behaviour is learnt and can be changed, or a Freudian-style analyst who believes that our early childhood experiences define us from the age of 5. The radical behaviourist is naïve and overly optimistic, whilst the Freudian analyst is more of an extreme pessimist. So how can we define a behaviour change strategy? A behaviour change strategy has been defined as 'changes in intensity, frequency or episodic severity that maintain across situations and time' (McDonnell and Anker, 2009). Strategies which aim to change behaviour tend to be long-term in nature. There are always opportunities to change our own behaviour, but as we get older it becomes increasingly difficult to change our behavioural characteristics. Think of the many bad habits you have acquired over the years. How easy is it to change them? There is a general agreement that people do struggle with their weight. It is not uncommon to read about obesity epidemics, and people talking about weight loss and diets. It would appear that, as people get older, the effectiveness of diets seems to become weakened, regardless of which diet is undertaken (Bray et al., 2018). This would suggest that behaviour change strategies are not as straightforward as they seem.

Can Good Behaviour Management Result in Change?

Behaviour management is intended to reduce the frequency or intensity of behaviours of concern without necessarily producing an enduring change in the individual. It has been argued that since crisis management procedures do not attempt to teach the individual a new behaviour, that behavioural change cannot occur (Carr et al., 1994). However, if behavioural change is defined more narrowly as a reduction in the frequency of a behaviour, then it could be claimed that behaviour change can occur. However, this definition would be problematic to use in research and has not been widely applied.

Do All Behaviours Need to Be Changed?

One argument which has to be considered within the context of behaviour of concern is whether all behaviours *need* to be changed. All behaviour is meaningful, communicative and occurs for a reason. Behaviour of concern can be viewed as a result and means of expressing an unmet need. When observing a behaviour, a carer should ask themselves the question, 'why does the person need to engage in the behaviour?' (Pitonyak, 2005) It is also important to consider the function of the behaviour for the individual, e.g. sensation seeking or sensation avoiding. When considering the need and function of a behaviour, it may become clear to a carer that behavioural change is not necessary. While changing behaviours of concern should always be a desirable outcome, behaviour management may be sufficient for some people. Consider the example of a young man with autism who repeatedly asks the same question to staff. Changing this behaviour may involve a range of strategies. However, from a behaviour management perspective, if the young man repeats the question 20 or 30 times before he can continue with an activity, is this really a problem? It is not uncommon that everyday behaviours may not require specific interventions. In contrast, repeated use of physical interventions or mechanical restraints would be undesirable if they remained unaltered.

Key Learning Questions:

1) Can you think of some strategies that might help to enhance carer tolerance levels?

2) Think of a behaviour of concern you have witnessed recently. Now consider why the person displaying the behaviour may have needed to engage in that behaviour.

3) Recall a challenging incident you were involved in recently, and think about how stress or trauma may have had an impact on or even caused the incident.

4) How can we explain to people that they often cause behaviours of concern without realising it?

CHAPTER 2

STRESS AND COPING

The aim of this chapter is to help practitioners understand and cope with both their own and other people's stress in care environments. Due to the difficulties faced within caring situations, being stressed can become a common occurrence for many practitioners and service users. Under stressful circumstances such as these, being able to recognise when you are stressed and to effectively use coping strategies is crucial for self-care. After all, how can we care for others if we are not caring for ourselves? In this chapter, we will explore what stress is, how it can present and how to cope with stress using practical coping strategies. As with the previous chapter, there is a questionnaire provided for the reader at the end, which you are encouraged to use to investigate your own level of stress at present.

There are also useful reflective and practical activities provided throughout which can be used to assist in managing stress.

What Is Stress?

Many models of stress have been developed. One of the most widely used was developed by US researchers Richard Lazarus and Susan Folkman (1984). They defined stress as a relationship between a person and the environment which is seen by the person as taxing, exceeding their resources, or endangering their well-being. This means that when we come across a stressor or threat that we feel we cannot deal with, our body reacts with both a biological and psychological response.

First, we perceive the stressor or threat and evaluate whether we able to cope with it. If this demand exceeds our resources, a stress response is triggered. The autonomic nervous system is activated, and increased levels of the stress hormones Adrenaline and Cortisol are released. The autonomic nervous system also controls body functions such as heart rate, respiration, body temperature and fear responses. When we become stressed, this results in our pulse and blood pressure increasing, as well as our breathing changing its rhythm and volume. We begin to sweat and can become easily startled. The sympathetic nervous system takes immediate action to mobilize these systems. In contrast, the parasympathetic nervous system focuses on activities that do not require immediate action.

This leads to fight, flight or freeze responses, which will be discussed in depth later. Our body reacts to the threat and becomes alert, and in a matter of seconds we appraise our situation and decide whether to fight, run away or to freeze, rooting ourselves to the spot. All of this occurs in split seconds of time. These responses to stressors are a basic part of all human physiology. From an evolutionary perspective, we require systems that will warn and alert us about threats to avoid being killed in the age of sabre-toothed tigers and other fearsome predators.

Even if we believe that we are good at managing highly stressful situations, the long-term impact of constantly triggering the warning system in the body can lead to negative effects on our physical and emotional well-being. For example, the hormone cortisol is secreted after the initial threat is detected, which creates a physiological response commonly known as an 'adrenaline rush'. Adrenaline reduces quite rapidly, but cortisol remains, maintaining our alertness which is valuable to our survival. If you are in a risky situation, you want to maintain an alert status and be vigilant that there are no more threats, even after the initial threat has passed. Here is a real-life example of how these physiological processes can function on an individual level:

'Late one night I was awoken from my sleep by a loud banging and crashing sound in the kitchen downstairs. I experienced a heightened state of arousal and a surge of adrenaline, followed by the thought, 'Is someone in my house?' Instead of calling the police, I listened intently to check if I heard more sounds, my alertness most likely aided by the spike in my cortisol levels. Upon hearing no more unusual sounds, I decided to sneak downstairs to investigate myself. My mind was racing: 'What if there are burglars in my house? What should I do? How many of them are there?' Had I been thinking instead of catastrophising, I might have made a lot of noise and turned on all the lights in an effort to scare the intruder away. In hindsight, I was probably using System 1 thinking, and therefore not really thinking sensibly at all. My cortisol levels were very high

indeed. I was hyperalert for any more sounds, but still the only thing I could hear was the washing machine on a spin cycle. Upon further investigation, it became clear that the crashing noise was made by a number of objects which had been on top of the washing machine. Sometime after switching the machine on before bed, the objects place on top of it had fallen to the ground with the movement of the drum. It took me nearly half an hour to get back to sleep as cortisol was surging through my system.'

The above example demonstrates the function of cortisol and adrenaline. People who are highly stressed may experience similar reactions to the most minor, everyday events. People who are hyperreactive may, over a period of months and years, experience the long-term negative effects of stress. There are many different types of stressors present in our lives, and the impact these can have on ourselves and the individuals we support is huge. Different stressors affect people in different ways; for some, a stressor such as running out of time to do a task can cause an immediate stress response, whereas for others, this may not be something that causes them stress.

Common stressors in life may include losing a loved one, family issues and difficulties with employment. In care settings, common stressors for staff could be supporting an individual who presents with behaviours of concern, safeguarding concerns or difficulties between colleagues. Of the individuals we support, some may not be able to inform us of their stressors, which is why having a support team who understands the individual and is able to advocate for them is fundamental. Sensory differences, difficulties with social situations and memory issues are only a few of the difficulties service users can face on a daily basis. Get to know the people you support well, understand what they find stressful and support them by implementing coping strategies. The benefits of doing so will be visible for all of their supporters. The question is, how do we know when people are stressed?

How Stressed Are You?

Sometimes we may be able to recognise that we are reaching the end of our resources to cope with stressful environments. On other occasions, we may need the observation of someone who is close to us to recognise that we are stressed, and to offer us support. The individuals we work with are no different, and whilst on some occasions they may be able to reduce their stress independently, there may be many times where they require our help to do so. Take some time to think about a service user you work with. How do you know when they are becoming stressed? What are the signs you look out for? These signs may be subtle or easily visible, and identifying them is beneficial to the individual and those who support them. Being able to recognise and reduce an individual's stress can have a significant impact on their emotional and physical well-being. My colleagues and I at Studio3 like to call this a 'stress signature'. An individual's stress signature is highly personal (similar to a fingerprint), and recognising how this has an impact can be very important in reducing stress. This is especially true if you can recognise early signs of stress. Let us look at the following example:

'Sarah is a nineteen-year-old girl who lives on her own with one-to-one staff in an acute setting. Formerly, she had been in a children's service. There were multiple diagnostic labels given to Sarah, including personality disorder and Asperger's syndrome. Many of Sarah's behaviours, which included self-injury and aggression, were

46

viewed as deliberate and wilful by members of her family and support staff. Sarah regularly used words such as 'stressed' and 'anxious', but it is clear she did not always know what those words meant. Sarah was encouraged to physically monitor her own heart rate, which was found to be consistently very high, introducing her to the biology of stress. Sarah was encouraged to increase her levels of physical exercise, and given a stress diary to identify times when she was stressed and encourage her to discuss this with her staff. It was clear that Sarah struggled to recognise a number of bodily sensations. Rather than internalising her stress, her staff described her as 'bouncing around like a pinball'. It was helpful that her supporters understood that many of her behaviours could be explained by her responses to stress. In Sarah's situation, she would struggle with recognising and interpreting changes in her heartbeat. She was also sensitive to the stress of her supporters. Interventions then began to focus on her supporter's stress management, rather than focusing on Sarah's stress directly.'

Thinking of how stress communicates across an organisation is also extremely important. We often find that stress is contagious (otherwise known as emotional contagion); that is, it can easily spread, especially when it comes to behaviours of concern. Targeting the sources of stress rather than focusing on distressed behaviour works well. Recent studies applying Mindfulness-based techniques with care staff have shown interesting results. The lead researcher in this field, Nirbhay Singh, found in a series of studies that Mindfulness training for carers reduced reported incidents of behaviour of concern (Singh et al., 2006). This would imply that carers who implement relatively simple relaxation and breathing techniques reduce their stress levels, which in turn has a positive impact on how they support people who are really challenging. It is also possible that when people practice these techniques, they become more accepting of behaviours of concern and view them as less of a problem. In the latter instance, their perception has changed. I myself have experienced staff teams working in care environments with distressed individuals who have reduced their own stress, and as a result are less concerned about behaviours of concern.

In an organisational context, it may be important to create positive role models. Team leaders who routinely support people presenting with behaviours of concern may need to be seen working directly with that individual and role modelling stress management techniques. It is also very clear that there are a wide range of stress management techniques that can be applied, not just Mindfulness. In terms of stress management, these can include the Relaxation Response developed by Herbert Benson, or progressive muscle relaxation to name but a few (Benson, 1975; Jacobson, 1929). In my experience, people who work in challenging environments tend to be quite poor at managing their own stress, and would benefit from being more aware of their own stressors.

However, it is not surprising that people are sometimes poor judges of their own stress. The following example is a fairly typical source of everyday stress:

'You are walking home after a relatively good day at work having finished all of your work for the week. It's Friday night and you feel great! You open the front door and hear your partner and your teenage child arguing. They are not shouting or talking loudly but the argument is heated and intense. As you walk into the house, you hear that they are disagreeing about their relationship and upcoming

plans. You are about to walk into the living room where they are arguing... How do you feel?'

In the above scenario, most people would feel a heightened level of stress. Now ask yourself, 'How could I enter that room and change the focus of the argument?' Take a few minutes to think about this. Now look at the following simple solutions:

1. Do not enter the room (avoidance).

2. Enter the room and join the argument.

3. Spend 30 seconds to 1 minute breathing slowly and calming yourself (role model calmness).

Most people, when they think about it, would choose option 3. Sadly, option 2 is probably the most common choice in reality. Why is this so important? The answer is relatively simple: in care environments, you may often witness two people arguing or even threatening each other. Depending on how stressed you are, you may rush in with the best intentions in the world and only make things worse. Even taking a few moments to gather your thoughts and appear calm can make a huge difference to what happens next.

The stress experienced by those around us can cause us to feel stressed as well. These transactions of stress occur often, sometimes without us even knowing it has. In care settings, this transaction can occur between carers and service users. Corbett et al. (2009) found that higher levels of cortisol in the evening appeared to be associated with high stress levels reported by parents. This suggests that a stressed carer can increase the stress of the individual they are supporting and vice versa. Therefore, as practitioners, reducing the stress we experience can positively influence not only our own well-being, but that of the people we support. Consider the following example:

'The McVicar family consists of Dad (32-year-old labourer) and Mum (28-year-old school teacher). They have 4 children - Joey (14), Michael (11), Lottie (8) and Suzy (4). Joey is labelled as dyslexic, Michael is diagnosed as being on the autism spectrum, Lottie seems to be thriving (no diagnosis) and there are suspicions that Suzy was beginning to struggle at school. The local social worker visited the home and described it as something akin to Lord of the Flies. *Dad worked usually until 9pm and Mum struggled to keep some semblance of control. There was little structure. Mealtimes were described as 'chaotic'. It was decided to adopt a stress plan for the family, and a routine was established whereby the children ate their dinner in two separate groups (Michael and Lottie in one group, Suzy and Joey in another). Mum and Dad were given stress management skills in the form of Mindfulness.'*

Understanding how stressed you are is vital in developing good coping strategies. Recognising your own stress is the cornerstone of this approach. We are very good at recognising stress in other people, but poorer in identifying it in ourselves. The next section will focus on how you recognise your own stress.

Recognising Your Own Stress

How do you know you are stressed? What signs show that you are stressed? It may be beneficial to ask people close to you how they know when you are stressed. Their answers may surprise you, and give you an insight into how you present when stressed. You may not realise what your signs are, but having this knowledge may help you to better recognise when you are stressed in future. This may also help identify your stressors and how they impact your overall level of stress. It is also important to note that the individuals you work with may be aware of your stress signs too, and that this could impact the way they interact with you when you are stressed.

There are many different measures of general stress levels. The following represents some key items adapted from a number of stress measures. It will give you a simple overview of your own stress level. It may also help you recognise some of the conditions that determine your stress, i.e. your stressors.

Complete the checklist below by assigning each statement a number from 1-5 to indicate their frequency in your life:

1- Never, 2- Rarely, 3- Sometimes, 4- Often, 5- Almost Always

1. I have a lot of worries at home

2. I have a lot of worries at school

3. People make too many demands of me

4. I know when I'm stressed

5. I know what my body feels like when I'm stressed

6. I don't understand what people want of me

7. I do not have enough time to pursue my interests

8. I have difficulty expressing how I feel about situations or people

9. I have trouble focusing on a task

10.   I have difficulty communicating with others

11.   I prefer to handle most things alone

12.   I do not have enough say in the decisions that affect me

13.   My personal needs are in conflict with my family

14.   My life is one crisis after another

15.   I regularly have headaches (2-5 times per week)

16.   I have muscle tension in my shoulder, neck or back

17.   I have stomach pains, indigestion or other digestive problems

18.   I regularly take aspirin, indigestion medication, sleeping pills or tranquilizers

19.   I have a tendency to overreact

20.   Most of my time is spent sitting/I get little exercise

21.   I would like to make changes in my life but do not know how

Now add up your responses for a total score.

What Was Your Score?

Total score of 34 or less: Good – Congratulations! Your stress level is low.

Total score of 35-65: Average – Lowering your stress level would be beneficial.

Total score of 66-85: Bad – Think seriously about making changes in your life to reduce stress.

Total score of 86 or higher: Dangerous – You need to act now to reduce stress!

Take some time to reflect on your score. Has your score surprised you? It is higher or lower than you expected? We often go through life trying to get through the day and our 'to-do lists'. Take some time to think about your own stress and whether you give much thought to this in your daily life. Which actions are required for you to maintain or increase your well-being? Which coping strategies could you use to reduce your stress? The next section describes some simple coping mechanisms for you to consider implementing in your life.

Coping With Stress

Stress simply cannot be discussed without considering how we cope with it. Lazarus and Folkman (1984) detailed that the impact of stress depends on how well we cope, what our coping styles are like and how effective they are. This highlights just how important our coping responses can be. Coping responses have been defined as cognitions (thoughts) and behaviours that a person uses to respond to stress and to moderate its emotional impact (Lazarus and Folkman, 1980). Take a moment to think about how you cope with stress. Would you say that your current coping responses are effective? When we are stressed, we advertently or inadvertently have ways to help us reduce this stress, but could these methods be improved, and what impact on our stress levels could this have? The benefits would not only impact our own well-being but that of those we support too. Now take some time to think about the individuals you support. How do they communicate their stress to you? What are their coping responses and are they effective in helping reduce their stress?

Think about how you can support the individuals you work with to continue to reduce their stress. What strategies can you implement to help those you support cope with stress? What steps could you take to record this information for new members of staff and other professionals to ensure that this vital information is shared?

The key to stress is not just to identify it, but to do something about it. A strong focus on coping strategies is always a positive approach. In my own work, I have found that producing a stress support plan can be far more meaningful that producing a behaviour support plan. The very expression 'stress support plan' implies that it is a collaborative approach. Such plans need to identify ways to reduce not just the individual's stress, but your own stress as well. Behaviour support plans, on the other hand, often focus far too much on targeting specific behaviours rather than a generalised approach to well-being. As has been pointed out in this chapter, it may well be more effective for carers to focus on their own stress first rather than targeting the behaviour of the individuals they support.

Developing these detailed plans should be a collaborative approach. Where possible, a stress support plan should always be worked on with the person you are supporting. Whilst I do not wish to be too prescriptive, it is typical for these plans to contain a number of elements. The plan should include a list of activities that can proactively reduce stress based on the individual's preferences, including Mindfulness, sensory diet, flow activities and exercise. There should also be a strong focus on coping strategies. One good example is often to ask people how they would prefer to be managed when they are experiencing a crisis and in some cases are 'melting down'. This can also be helpful when developing cultures of restraint reduction.

There are many different ways to cope with stress. Lazarus and Folkman (1984) identified two major types of coping; problem-focused and emotion-focused. The following example demonstrates how problem-focused coping can help people achieve goals whilst reducing stress:

'Frederick is fifteen years old and has problems including school attendance and aggression in the family home. Frederick has multiple diagnoses, including ADHD and dyslexia. A recent neurological investigation also suggested that epilepsy might be a factor. He has five siblings who are younger than him. Frederick finds it difficult to cope with the behaviours of his younger brothers, and he often shouts at them and hits them if they enter his bedroom. Frederick was recently allocated two specialist workers to try to increase his school attendance, and to engage him in evening activities outside of the family home. His stress levels were very high, and it was decided by his team to develop a stress support plan which focused on cardiac exercise. Most of his cardiac goals were non-social and took the form of jogging with his support staff, usually later in the evenings. It had been decided that gyms were places that overstimulated him. Frederick developed a good relationship with his two workers and agreed that he would like to eventually take part in a half marathon. His support staff changed the goal to running a 10-kilometre route with them within 3 months. Frederick achieved this goal within the time frame. His school attendance has improved, as has his sustained sleep time. It has been noted by his teaching staff that he is beginning to show signs of sustained learning.'

Whilst there are no claims that all aspects of his life improved, the focus on cardiac exercise appeared to help him regulate his stress and arousal levels. In addition, it gave a strong focus on achievable goals. It also removed him from the house at key times. This example illustrates how using exercise as a primary intervention helped to create a window for meaningful engagement. A good stress plan should have simple goals to alleviate stress. In Frederick's situation, there had been a series of attempts to teach him stress management skills which included both cognitive behavioural therapy (CBT) and Mindfulness. Engaging him in an achievable goal that did not require group-based collaboration appeared to be the key to his stress management.

Conclusions

To conclude, this chapter focused on the definition of stress as well as common stressors in daily life and care settings. The implications of these on an individual's stress levels were discussed. This chapter also looked at different coping strategies for dealing with stress. The key message from this chapter is that, in order to adopt a low arousal approach, a person must be able to recognise and respond to their own stress levels whilst also being able to help the people they support to do the same. Through reflection and proactive strategies, we can ensure that the settings we work in become low stress environments, thus enabling us as practitioners to continue to support individuals for the long-term.

Key Learning Questions

1) What is stress?
2) How do you recognise when you are stressed?
3) How do you recognise stress in other people? Are there universal signals of stress, or can these be unique to individuals?
4) How can you reduce your own stress?

CHAPTER 3

TRAUMA

A traumatic event is loosely defined as a deeply distressing or disturbing experience. Under this definition, there are several life events which could be classed as traumatic. If the person experiencing the event perceives it to be very distressing and disturbing, then it is classed as a traumatic event for them. It is important to recognise the role of perception within this area. What one individual may find distressing and disturbing may be different to another, especially if they have had several traumatic events in their life. There is often an overemphasis placed on trauma being caused by major, triggering life events. For someone who is highly distressed, an event which may be perceived as a relatively minor issue to an outsider can in fact be traumatic to an individual. A person's past experiences and current levels of stress are therefore important factors in how they perceive life events. A person who is developmentally young and has a poor concept of space and time may become highly stressed and traumatised if a significant person leaves the room.

Trauma and Stress

As previously discussed in this book, if we perceive a stressor or threat and evaluate that the demands of this threat exceed our resources, a stress response is triggered, resulting in the fight, flight or freeze response. For an individual who is highly stressed and is constantly on the verge of experiencing this response, they may be more vigilant of stressors or threats around them. They may perceive these stressors as a major threat to their safety and feel that they must fight or run away from the situation for their own welfare. However, from someone else's perspective, the stressor may seem harmless and the reaction excessive. An individual who has experienced trauma is highly vigilant of further threats to their safety, and will rely on their stress response to keep them safe. Stress and trauma are fundamentally linked, and as an individual's stress level falls, they become less vigilant to what they feel are further threats, and may eventually reach a point where they feel able to talk about their past traumatic experiences.

Trauma and PTSD

Post-traumatic stress disorder (PTSD) can be a chronic and disabling condition which can deeply impact an individual's life. Within the Diagnostic and Statistical Manual of Mental Disorders (DSM-5), PTSD is classified as a trauma and stress-related disorder (American Psychiatric Association, 2013). These disorders are unique in that diagnosis requires the individual to have been exposed to an extreme stressor such as threat of death, serious injury or sexual violence. Common symptoms of PTSD are described as:

- Reliving aspects of the event, including having flashbacks, intrusive thoughts, nightmares, distress and physical symptoms such as pain, sweating, shaking etc.

- Alertness or feeling on edge. This can include feelings of panic, anger, being upset and hypervigilant, as well as lack of sleep, poor concentration and increased irritability.

- Avoiding feelings or memories. This can include trying to stay busy, avoiding items which remind you of the event, lack of feeling emotions, feeling cut off, finding it hard to express emotions etc.

- Difficult beliefs or feelings. This can include feeling like you can't trust anyone, nowhere is safe, others will not understand, blame, guilt, sadness, shame and anger.

Our understanding of PTSD has moved from a simple view whereby a clearly traumatic life event (such as 9/11) causes stress, to viewing stress as much more complex in nature.

Complex PTSD

Complex post-traumatic stress disorder (C-PTSD) or complex stress disorder is a psychological disorder that can develop in response to prolonged, repeated experience of interpersonal trauma in a context in which the individual has little or no chance of escape. It is associated with a wide range of conditions ranging from sexual and physical abuse to victims of human trafficking and slavery. Loss of control as well as isolation are crucial factors and an association with attachment is often mentioned.

The people we support may not necessarily be formally diagnosed, but they can still show a number of clear signs of trauma. Trauma can have an even greater impact on specific populations, although some of the evidence is limited. Mevissen and de Jongh (2011) point to evidence which suggests that people with intellectual disabilities are more likely to suffer from PTSD. Understanding the trauma process may sometimes involve a good understanding of a person's life story. We can refer to people having 'traumatic pasts' in this context. For three years, I worked with a forty-four-year-old man named Adam who had a complex and traumatic history. This is his story:

'Adam was supported by a staff team in a small community home. He had been labelled with a severe personality disorder, mood disorder and attachment issues. In his past, there had been several periods of hospitalisation, most of which was related to his difficulties coping on his own and a profound sense of lonleiness. Adam's current team found it difficult to emotionally cope with his 'explosive rages', which could be triggered by seemingly trivial things such as the post arriving with utility bills, or a reminder that a significant birthday was imminent. Adam could be arguing with you one minute and very quickly move on and appear quite calm. There were a number of past traumas which included being restrained by hospital staff and, on another occasion, being restrained by the police. Adam consistently made abuse allegations against others, often after he had been restrained. Eventually, Adam's early life history was revealed to the team (the files had been sealed to respect his privacy). Adam had been sexually abused by a family member at age twelve. At fifteen,

he was used as a child prostitute, with his Aunt acting as his agent. Adam had also witnessed extreme violence and experienced temporary homelessness on several occasions. As an adult, Adam rarely had contact from his own family and he would constantly tell people that he was lonely. Paradoxically, he also seemed to struggle to be around people for prolonged periods of time. His sleep was often disturbed. Though he never really spoke about why, he often woke up in the night, and some staff reported hearing him scream and shout "No!"'

Adam's traumatic history was enough to explain the failure of many well-intentioned attempts to provide psychological interventions, ranging from CBT and dialectical behaviour therapy (DBT), to a number of attempts at various psychotherapies. The latter approach did have some success in terms of his own understanding of his behaviour. Adam consistently burnt out staff teams, but things began to improve when they were given contextual and historical information about his life traumas. This helped individuals to understand his explosivity, as he was clearly experiencing what trauma victims describe as 'flashbacks'. Sadly, Adam died of a very sudden heart attack. At the young age of forty-four, I believe that his death was caused by a combination of his difficulties in regulating his own arousal and the effects of long-term trauma.

Trauma-Based Long-Term Interventions

Trauma symptoms can have a huge impact on individuals and the people who support them. However, with the right support, people can recover from traumatic life events. Support through psychological therapies has shown positive outcomes and effects. Cohen, Deblinger, Mannarino and Steer (2004) found that children who received trauma-focused cognitive behavioural therapy (TF-CBT) demonstrated significantly more improvement with regard to PTSD, depression, behaviour problems, shame, and abuse-related attributions compared to those who received child-centred therapy. Whist there are many trauma-based therapies for children and adults, the PACE (playfulness, acceptance, curiosity and empathy) model developed by the American psychologist Dan Hughes has perhaps the closest fit with the low arousal approach (Hughes et al., 2019). The model draws from psychotherapy and attachment-based frameworks. A cornerstone of the model is the communication of empathy and acceptance of the child in an environment that can contain (emotionally and physically) the young person. There is a strong emphasis on relationship building to help the person develop healthy attachments with caregivers or parents. The positive aspect of this approach is that there is a clear message that people who are traumatised can be helped to recover. There are clear parallels with working with adults. It is important to work on developing relationships that foster a sense of containment and safety, whether a person is in a care or home support situation. In the UK, my colleague Dr. John McDermott has been applying this model to groups who support people with autism. This is an empowering style of communication, whereby the individual is placed at the centre of the approach by developing a strong line of communication between themselves and their supporters. Similarly, an adapted version of the model has been applied to the training and coaching of foster carers in the UK by my colleagues David Walker and David Jones. In their work, they have emphasised that developing positive relationships with traumatised children (or adults) requires a balance between compassion and acceptance. I have experience of working with highly stressed and traumatised individuals who often require safe, restraint-free environments. Low arousal approaches to crisis management can provide healthy containment within a philosophy of humanism, as is demonstrated in the following example:

'Eric is a fourteen-year-old boy who was physically abused by his father as a young child. He has been placed in a number of children's services, where he often ran away. He has also been exposed to a variety of control methods, including a variety of sanctions-based methods. It is very clear that physical restraint in the form of prone and supine holds had been used in former placements. His current fostering parents have been trained in trauma-informed and low arousal approaches. This means that his parents have been taught to avoid physical restraint and allow Eric to learn to self-regulate by encouraging him to walk off his anger, or even break minor objects. It was explained to him that the first rule he had to learn was not to hit people, but that expressing his anger verbally was OK. This was to encourage him to develop self-control strategies. His foster family were also encouraged to avoid engaging in debates with him, especially when he was in a highly aroused state. After three months, the intensity of his stress-related behaviours decreased, which created the space for him to begin to openly communicate with his foster family about his needs.'

Everyday 'Invisible Trauma'

Trauma may take more subtle forms. If a person does not appear to have had any exposure to an obvious external trauma, people may be 'context blind' and fail to consider that the impact of relatively everyday, routine behaviours can be traumatising to the person. Consider the following example:

'Juanita is a seventeen-year-old girl with a diagnosis of severe intellectual disability. Juanita is considered to be kind and considerate most of the time, but there have been instances where she can become very aggressive. Verbal communication issues lead to her becoming frustrated at times when she is unable to make her needs and wants clear. There are other times where her behaviour appears to have no obvious triggers. It has been noted that Juanita will often cry when certain people leave her line of sight. Sometimes, the loss of a favourite toy leads to excessive periods of crying.'

In Juanita's situation, her developmentally young understanding made it difficult for her to comprehend that objects and people existed in space and time. Her thinking was focused on the 'here and now'. The team supporting her used a reassuring approach that could at best be described as well-intentioned. They were advised to stop using words that were not related to the present, as statements like 'she has gone to the shops and will be back' often made her crying worse. Distraction was very effective, for example offering her a snack or a drink, or singing a favourite nursery rhyme. The key to interacting with Juanita was focusing on a 'now and next' style of communication that pre-warned her of events before they occurred so as to reduce their traumatic impact.

People with other conditions, such as acquired brain injuries (ABI), may experience loss and trauma over the removal of a preferred object. The following example from many years ago demonstrates how necessary compassion and understanding is when working with traumatised individuals:

'Bill was a fifty-two-year-old man who lived in a long-term care hospital after a routine operation to remove a benign brain tumour

went badly wrong. Bill suffered oxygen starvation which left him with partial paralysis of his body and memory problems. Bill would keep old records in a suitcase under his bed. He would often ask people to search for a specific record and show it to him. A young nursing assistant was advised by more experienced staff to 'ignore him - he eventually will calm down'. The other advice was to 'tell him you have the record without even looking in his suitcase'. The young nursing assistant decided to ignore all of this advice because it 'felt wrong'. When he heard Bill shouting, he would rush to his room and search for the requested record. All he had to do was show it to Bill and he would immediately calm down. After only six weeks of working with Bill, a senior matron asked him why his relationship with Bill was so positive. He told her the truth about what he had been doing and she immediately understood, saying, "Some of my colleagues suffer from compassion fatigue". She also advised that the young nursing assistant should listen to his gut more often.'

I was the person in the above example and, with the benefit of hindsight, I now realise that it had a profound impact on my choice of career.

Trauma-Informed Behaviour Management

Trauma-informed work means developing an understanding of how trauma works, including how events can re-traumatise individuals. Helping an individual to reduce their stress levels and being mindful of their past traumas is key when supporting others. Think of a service user you support, thinking back to their records and past reports which may detail traumatic life events and abuse they have experienced. This would have been a very difficult time for them, and the impact is long-lasting. Consider the history of the person;

were they subject to physical or verbal aggression, use of sanctions? As a practitioner, re-traumatising the individual should be avoided in any way possible.

A good example of trauma-informed behaviour management involves individuals who have been exposed to excessive restrictions or prolonged restraints in the past. Those individuals may be transported back to their traumatised past and experience the same feelings of fear when they are restrained in any manner which is reminiscent of past restraints. I was once asked by a young man living in a community service about my views on physical restraint. He wanted to show and describe to me the many ways that he had been restrained by staff. He was confused by the fact that he saw many of the staff as his friends and had a good time with them, but then, if he broke a rule or tried to leave, they would restrain him. He described a whole variety of 'hold downs' which he could recall in great detail, and became extremely distressed, telling me that he did not want to think about them anymore.

Many people we support have a history of restraints being used to manage their behaviour, but we must be vigilant that continued use of restraint only serves to re-traumatise them. Restraint reduction is vital for these individuals in order to prevent further trauma. How can you develop a trusting relationship if you are also using restraint? I accept that many readers may now label me as a bleeding-heart liberal. I also accept that members of the police may be faced with situations where they have to restrain an individual in order to keep people safe. However, the examples in this book involve building relationships with individuals, and, in my view, restraint is an obvious barrier to this. Working in a trauma-informed manner enables practitioners to limit the use of restraints, and enable individuals to live restriction and restraint-free lives. Trauma-informed behaviour management is therefore an important aspect to low arousal approaches (McDonnell, 2010). The next example demonstrates how individuals who have experienced trauma over prolonged periods of time can be easily 're-traumatised' by simple everyday practices:

'Sadie is a fourteen-year-old young person who lives with her long-term foster family. Sadie had originally been taken from her family home aged only three years old due to suspicions of physical abuse and neglect from both of her parents. For nearly two years, Sadie lived a semi-secure specialist environment. The staff managed her self-harm using restraint and a reward-based behaviour programme. Neither approach appeared to be that successful. Eventually, Sadie was placed with an experienced foster family. Her foster parents are advocates of the low arousal approach and also have a good understanding of trauma-informed behaviour management. Sadie thrives with their support, such that her attendance at school has improved and her self-harm has become intermittent, usually triggered by a specific issue.'

Trauma-informed behaviour management can also require a high degree of self-control and emotional regulation from supporters, as the following example demonstrates:

'Alex is a sixteen-year-old boy with a diagnosis of ADHD. He struggles to attend school, which has led to the involvement of the education authorities. Alex's parents describe him as being exceptionally difficult to manage at home. When a Studio3 practitioner conducted an assessment with the family, it was clear that they felt like they were losing control, and that the boundaries

they had placed on him actually seemed to be escalating the situation. Initially, his parents had adopted a 'tough love approach', whereby Alex had to comply with a set of house rules that included agreed bedtimes, a homework schedule, the sanctioning of swearing and physical confrontation. His favourite objects, such as his tablet and TV, had to be earned. Alex's response to this involved lower frequency behaviours that were far more intense. When his foster family eventually sought help from staff at Studio3, the approach they were trained to adopt was almost the opposite of the previous regime. Studio3 practitioners pointed to Alex's background and family history as a way of making sense of his behaviour. Alex had been in care until he was nine years of age. He had been witness to, and sometimes the victim of, physical abuse as a young child. His parents had adopted him after a process of fostering, and it was explained to them that Alex should be viewed as a traumatised young man. They were advised that the arguments they were having with him appeared to be re-traumatising him. They adopted a low arousal approach when supporting Alex which focused on avoiding arguments and debates wherever possible. The emphasis involved his adopted parents agreeing to fewer rules, and accepting that they needed to negotiate rather than make him obey. Initially, in the first few months, the parents found this approach difficult as they felt that they were being over-controlled by Alex. The reality is that both the intensity and frequency of incidents has dramatically reduced.'

Using knowledge of trauma and how it can impact an individual was crucial in understanding Alex's behaviour. His parents using practices which created further restrictions and boundaries served to not only escalate his behaviour, but further traumatise him. Having an understanding of Alex's trauma history was key towards establishing methods of managing his behaviour which would not re-traumatise him. It was clear from Alex's statements and how explosive his behaviours were that it was a result of his traumatic history. By adopting a low arousal approach, Alex was not further re-traumatised but better supported by those around him. They gained a deeper understanding as to why Alex was reacting in the way he was, and supported him to find alternative means to express himself.

How can the reader of this book improve their trauma-informed practice? The following exercise may be of help.

Think of a time in your life where you either experienced a traumatising situation or dealt with a loss or bereavement.

Try to answer the following questions:

1) Did the trauma/loss cause physical sensations of pain?

2) How long did it take for you to adjust to the trauma/loss?

3) What were the recurring thoughts and feelings that you remember?

4) What situations or events re-triggered these thoughts and feelings?

When reflecting on these answers, try to think about the way trauma had an impact on you and the lives of people around you. How did you resolve these issues?

An important skill in this process is empathy, and making an effort to emotionally connect with stressed or traumatised individuals. In the next chapter, we will think about the role of empathic understanding.

Key Learning Questions

1) What do you understand by the word 'trauma'?

2) What is everyday 'invisible' trauma, and how can this affect people's behaviour?

3) What is trauma-informed behaviour management, and why is it so important to view distressed individuals as being stressed and traumatised?

4) Think about some of the strategies that can be used to manage trauma. How could you apply these to your own work?

CHAPTER 4

EMPATHY

This chapter aims to define what empathy is, and why empathy is important when using low arousal approaches. As with the previous chapters, there is also a questionnaire provided for the reader which can be used to work out your current level of empathy. When this empathy score has been established, there are further reflective and practical activities provided which can be used to help you to become more empathic.

What is Empathy?

The concept of empathy does not have a single definition. Rather, a number of definitions are known regarding its construct (Coll et al., 2017). What is universally agreed upon is that, for empathy to occur, the empathiser (person aiming to be empathetic) and target of empathy (person they are aiming to show empathy towards) should be in a similar state (Cuff et al., 2016; Decety and Jackson, 2004; de Vignemont and Singer, 2006; de Waal, 2008; Zaki and Ochsner, 2012). To put it simply, to be empathetic requires you to be able to place yourself in someone else's shoes, and to understand what they would be thinking and feeling in that situation. Have you ever felt truly connected to someone? That they understood how you felt in a situation and why you felt that way, as well as sharing that feeling? This is empathy in practice.

It is arguably quite difficult to meet and work with people without experiencing some form of empathy towards them. However, sometimes the individuals we support struggle with empathy, due either to their past experiences and failing to learn social skills, or due to neuro-developmental conditions which can make empathising with others difficult. An example of how some individuals can struggle with empathy is demonstrated by the following case study:

'Diana is a twenty-six-year-old woman who has a diagnosis of Autism Spectrum Disorder (ASD). She was referred to Studio3 after having issues with her support team. When we met with Diana, it was soon clear that she struggled with empathy. This is not to say that Diana was in any way purposefully impolite or rude. Diana often felt guilty when she was made aware that she had caused upset or concern to the staff members or others. On these occasions, she simply struggled to be able to see a situation from another person's point of view. This difficulty to empathise, and being unable to determine how what she said or did could make others feel, often resulted in people perceiving her as rude or unkind. For example, one day a support worker changed their hairstyle. When they arrived on shift, Diana noticed this and stated that the staff member had

changed their hair. The staff member thanked Diana for noticing and asked what she thought. Diana answered rather bluntly that she thought it looked much nicer before, and advised her to get her money back. This understandably upset the support worker, who told her manager that Diana had been rude to her. Diana was upset when this was communicated to her, as she had not meant to be rude. She explained that she was trying to be helpful by answering the support worker's question truthfully, and giving her advice. It was clear from this situation that, due to her difficulties with empathy, Diana could not understand why her comments had upset her support worker.'

Empathy Difficulties Are Not Limited to Distressed People

Staff members and teams can struggle with empathy too. Whilst we may think that we are empathic practitioners, it is difficult to be empathetic all of the time. Mentally and emotionally we can 'clock out' of our work, like the staff member in the following example:

'In a care organisation early one morning, the clock turned from 8:59 to 9:00. The office phone rang and the person on call at the organisation answered. The individual calling wished to communicate that they were feeling unwell. The staff member taking the call informed them that their on-call shift was now over, and that they were sorry but the individual would have to call back when the next member of staff had begun their shift.'

In this example, the staff member was not being intentionally mean or cruel. However, in that moment, they were not being empathetic. They showed sympathy by apologising, but failed to place themselves in the client's shoes and demonstrate empathy.

Damian Milton in the UK has argued that when supporting people on the autism spectrum, carers often experience what he describes as a 'double empathy problem' (Milton, 2017). This means that carers can struggle to empathise with some individuals due to a lack of understanding of their difficulties. Sometimes, it can be simply a lack of experience that leads to this situation. A good example of this is when a person who has never really experienced overwhelming stress and hyperarousal may fail to recognise this in the person they support. Double empathy problems can also occur for specific populations more than others. If you work with people with acquired brain injuries (ABI) or older adults with dementia, you can always consider the possibility that this could be you at some point down the line. I recall a member of staff in an older adults' service saying the following on a training course:

"When I work with people with dementia, I am always thinking that in 30 to 40 years' time this could be me, lying in bed, confused and struggling to understand the world. I always remind myself of this when I get irritated or annoyed by a 'patient'."

Empathy issues can also highlight our own prejudices and biases. A good example of this occurred many years ago in a clinical meeting with a group of staff. They were discussing the management of an individual whose behaviour was highly verbally abusive to people and rarely apologetic. One member of staff really struggled with the fact that there was a lack of apology or apparent empathy towards them. It was very clear that they believed apologies were necessary as a product of their development and upbringing. The majority of the staff did not share this view, and told them, 'If you want an apology you will be waiting an awfully long time. Our client is really stressed and struggles to empathise with people - it's nothing personal.' When supporting highly distressed people, an understanding of double empathy issues is important as it can drive our understanding of people themselves.

Empathy and Sympathy

At this point you may be wondering the difference between empathy and sympathy. Whilst there has been great debate in this area, the general consensus is that they are separate concepts. Sympathy is defined as being a part of empathy, as sympathy requires you to acknowledge someone's sadness and feel 'pity', which may drive you to wish to help them (Baron-Cohen and Wheelwright, 2004). Empathy, on the other hand, goes a step further. Not only can you recognise their emotions (for example, sadness), but you can also put yourself in their shoes and acknowledge *why* they are sad in that situation. You can further know what they are thinking and how they must feel, acknowledging and sharing that emotion.

This difference can be demonstrated through the example of a friend having a bereavement. In this situation, if you felt sympathy for your friend you may offer condolences and state that you are sorry for their loss. Most likely you would feel pity for their sadness, and sad that they are upset. On the other hand, an empathic approach would require an understanding of how sad your friend truly is, acknowledging how that particular sadness would feel for them and what they must be thinking in that situation. From the example, the key difference between the empathy and sympathy approach can be seen; empathy requires a sharing of feeling rather than a separate feeling of pity. This is why we should aim to be empathic as opposed to sympathetic practitioners. Instead of wanting to help due to 'pity', we *can* help through a deeper understanding of and connection with our client.

Levels of Empathy

It is really important at this point to stress that individuals with lower levels of empathy are not emotionless. There are also differing levels of empathy, similar to Intellectual Quotient (IQ), and having low levels of empathy does not mean someone has no empathy. It does however mean that people with lower levels of empathy may need more help in this area to understand or learn how to be more empathetic. In fact, many people who have lower levels of empathy but are made aware of this are able to become slightly more empathic as a result. There are of course individuals with low levels of empathy who may commit crime, as they do not think about the impact of their actions on their victims. In some cases, once they are made aware of the consequences of their crime by meeting their victims and reflecting, they can change their behaviour. It is therefore best to think of empathy as a continuum. We should also remember that people behave differently in different situations.

For example, a person who truly loves animals, but is not necessarily regarded as a 'people person', may empathise with the suffering of animals more than the suffering of people. We often apply different rules to the behaviour of our own children than we do to other people's children. Recently, a colleague of mine commented on a member of staff working in a care setting who appeared to have difficulties empathising with some of the people they supported. Yet that same person outside of work was passionate about working with young children, especially through sport. Did they switch their empathic understanding off at work and then turn it back on in a different situation? We may never know, but the importance of using empathy across all areas in our life is central to the low arousal approach.

Why is Empathy Needed?

Let us take stock on what we have covered. We have explored what empathy is, what it looks like, and how the levels of empathy can differ between individuals. We have also clarified that a lack of empathy does not mean that someone is cruel. With this in mind, why is empathy needed to work with individuals who display behaviours of concern, and why should we aim to improve our levels of empathy? Take a look at the following example:

'Irving is a thirty-seven-year-old male client who has a traumatic history, and presents with a number of diagnoses. Working with Irving when he was stressed and displaying behaviours of concern can be both physically and emotionally exhausting. This is due to the fact that Irving, as well as being physically aggressive towards his staff and his environment, will often abscond into the community and walk for hours at a time. Additionally, Irving is known to be verbally abusive towards his support team when he is stressed. When staff first met with Studio3, they had great difficulty empathising with

Irving, which culminated in them feeling that Irving was purposefully aiming to hurt or upset them. A large part of the intervention with the staff team aimed to make them more empathetic towards Irving. This involved taking time with the staff team to reflect on situations and how Irving may have felt in that situation, as well as acknowledging times when they had become stressed or angry. Through this intervention, the staff team were able to understand how Irving was feeling and why he was becoming stressed. This resulted in a culture change within the support team, who instead began to approach Irving as a traumatised individual who could not control his actions when stressed. They are now also able to better identify Irving's sources of stress and reduce these. This intervention has led to a reduction in his behaviours of concern, due to being less stressed and having a better relationship with his support team.

Empathy and the Low Arousal Approach

As demonstrated in the case above, empathy is imperative when working with people who display behaviours of concern. This is also reflected in the low arousal approach, which denotes that we must aim to lower demands when someone is becoming stressed. Empathy is a key component of this, as it ensures that we are connected to the client and understand why and when our client is becoming stressed. Through the use of empathy, the practitioner is able to see the situation from the point of view of the client, and thus understand what trigger within the situation led to them feeling stressed and melting down. Furthermore, it is essential for the practitioner to acknowledge that the individual is unable to control their actions due to stress, instead of viewing their behaviour as purposeful. Empathy is therefore the first key element of the low arousal approach because without empathy, the low arousal approach cannot be practiced.

Therefore, the first and most important step towards becoming a low arousal practitioner is to first ensure that you are an empathic practitioner, and then to improve your current empathic skills and practice.

Empathy Questionnaire

As discussed above, empathy is a core element of the low arousal approach, and is vital to working with individuals who display behaviours of concern. The following questionnaire on empathy now gives you the opportunity to work out your own empathy levels (Spreng, et al., 2009). To get the most out of this manual, it is important that you try to be completely honest with yourself. If you struggle with this exercise, ask a good friend to examine the questions and tell you how they would answer if they were pretending to be you.

Below is a list of statements. Please read each statement carefully and rate how frequently you feel or act in the manner described. There are no right or wrong answers, or trick questions. Please answer each question as honestly as you can using the scale below:

Never – 0, Rarely – 1, Sometimes – 2, Often – 3, Always - 4

1) When someone else is feeling excited, I tend to get excited too

2) Other people's misfortunes disturb me a great deal

3) It upsets me to see someone being treated disrespectfully

4) I am affected when someone close to me is happy

5) I enjoy making other people feel better

6) I have tender, concerned feelings for people less fortunate than me

7) When a friend starts to talk about their problems, I do not try to steer the conversation towards something else

8) I can tell when others are sad even when they do not say anything

9) I find that I am 'in tune' with other people's moods

10) I feel sympathy for people who are the cause of their own serious illnesses

11) I become upset when someone else cries

12) I am interested in how other people feel

13) I get a strong urge to help when I see someone who is upset

14) When I see someone being treated unfairly, I feel pity for them

15) I do not find it silly for people to cry out of happiness

16) When I see someone being taken advantage of, I feel kind of protective towards them

What Was Your Score?

30 and below is a very low empathy quotient, indicating that you have a low level of empathy towards other people.

An average score for the majority of people would be somewhere in the area of 45.

50 and above would be a high empathy quotient, indicating that you have a high level of empathy for other people.

Do you feel that your result reflects how empathic you really are? Has it made you think about your own empathy? If yes, what has it encouraged you to consider?

Scoring these types of questionnaires can be very subjective. Try not to worry about the mathematics of your score - it is more important as a guide to make you think about your own empathy.

It is sometimes unhelpful to think of people as though they have little or no empathy. However, it is true that many people do struggle with empathic understanding, and quite often this can vary dramatically between situations. A person may be highly empathic when listening to a relative who has experienced a loss, but that same person may struggle to empathise with someone who assaulted them in work. The following exercise aims to focus on your own empathic understanding of a highly stressed individual. Think about an individual that you have successfully developed a positive relationship with, despite their distressed behaviours:

1) Why did you pick this person to be empathic towards? What was the situation and why was empathy required?

2) How did you show empathy towards them?

3) Did they appear to show empathy towards you?

4) Were you able to connect with this person? Could you share their feelings? What did you believe they were thinking, and could you understand and share this experience with them by perceiving the situation from their point of view?

We sometimes make connections with people without fully understanding why this has occurred. I have supported many people with distressed behaviours over the years, and it is always the case that there are people who can develop an empathic understanding of even the most highly distressed individuals in the most difficult circumstances. These individuals make an effort to 'see the person not the behaviours', even in the most fear-evoking situations. The next chapter will focus on the mechanism of fear, and how it can sometimes be a barrier to empathy.

Key Learning Questions

1) What do you understand by the term empathy?

2) How does empathy differ from sympathy?

3) Think of a time when you have developed an empathic understanding of a person you supported. What personal factors about them drove you to connect with them? What does this tell you about your own capacity for empathy?

4) Now, think of a time when you have felt unable to understand an individual's feelings and behaviours. How could you, as an empathic practitioner, work to establish an empathic understanding with that person?

UNDERSTANDING FEAR

This chapter aims to define fear, and to explain the psychological and physiological fear response. It will further demonstrate how our own fear can have a strong negative impact on our ability to support individuals. Allowing yourself to be exposed to fearful situations and respond in a low arousal manner requires both courage and bravery. There is also a questionnaire provided for the reader which can be used to work out your current level of fear in relation to working with a client or individual you support. When this fear score has been established there is a practical bravery exercise, which can be used to improve your current levels of bravery and to take another step towards becoming a Low Arousal Practitioner.

What is Fear?

Fear is a physical and emotional response to an object, person or situation that can often lead to panic. Fear is a psychological and physiological response that many would like to avoid in life. However, like 'moths attracted to the flame', people can grow to like the adrenaline rush that is associated with fear. First, let us focus on how and why fear occurs. Fear helps to keep us alive and safe. Without an element of fear in threatening situations, we would be prey to all kinds of predators (Harari, 2011). Research indicates that, as part of the evolutionary process, humans learned to react to dangerous situations; to become fearful, ensuring that they were protected and survived (Seligman, 1971). It could be argued that mankind is at the peak of the evolutionary tree, which means that in general we have few predators. The reality is that the fear response is a vital part of our survival mechanism. Any reader of this book can think of everyday fearful situations. Fear is evidently a necessary emotion and highly functional. But what causes the fear response to occur?

Within the brain there is an area which appears to be activated when an individual feels fear. This area of the brain is called the fear circuit. This area then sends messages to the other areas of th to prepare the individual for the threat (Sapolsky, 201 the body from the perceived threat, the brai physiological responses. This include body to heighten the individual' further increase their heart rate t of the body (Cannon, 1929). The can be overwhelming for people ar phobias, where we tend to practice t avoidance. It may seem a little strange that a book devoted to supporting distressed individuals should focus on fear responses, but we often expect people to expose themselves to highly fearful situations in our work. Therefore, understanding our responses to fear is very important to any person who regularly exposes themselves to fear.

The Psychological Response

There are three known psychological responses to fear: fight, flight and freeze (Gray, 1998). These psychological reactions are each ways in which individuals process fear, thus impacting on how the individual reacts to the threat. To discuss and explain each of the three responses, a scenario will now be outlined and each response discussed separately.

The Scenario

You are leaving a party after a great evening and are now walking home alone. It is two o'clock in the morning. It is dark, but you decide to take a short cut to save time. The only issue is that this route takes you away from the streetlights and main road, instead leading you down by the river under a dimly lit underpass. However, you are keen to get home, so you take the route. As you begin to pass through the underpass you hear a second set of footsteps behind you. As the footsteps increase in speed you see a shadow on the wall, outlining a figure coming closer, catching up with you. As you turn you see a figure, they shout at you to handover your wallet, closing the gap between you...'

Fight

Your first response may well be to fight. This means that when an individual perceives a threat, they decide to challenge it. Therefore, in this scenario, someone who has a fight response may decide to face the threat head on by fighting the attacker. The body prepares itself to fight as adrenaline surges, your pupils dilate and, depending on the situation, you may assume an aggressive stance. Your heart rate increases making you ready to respond. In these circumstances, you may refuse to give up your wallet and start to display physical aggression towards the figure. You may shout or threaten or, in some circumstances, you may physically attack the person. (The correct low arousal response is relatively simple - give them your wallet). Some individuals may deliberately increase their level of physiological arousal. Historically, the Vikings classified some of their most fearsome warriors as 'Berserkers'. Little is known about the rituals involved that led to them going berserk, but one can only assume it involved large amounts of alcohol. At the battle of Stamford Bridge in Yorkshire in 1066, the victorious Saxon army of King Harold was held up on the bridge by one Viking Berserker. This was the same King Harold who met a horrible death to William the Conqueror not long afterwards.

Flight

The second response is flight. This means that when an individual perceives a threat, they are psychologically programmed to go into flight mode, and put as much distance as possible between themselves and the threat. Your heart rate will be high and your adrenaline levels will also increase. Therefore, when applying the flight response to the above scenario, the individual may turn away from the figure and quickly run home. Their adrenaline levels may still be high and it is likely that they will experience a surge in their cortisol levels, which sustains a high level of alertness. I was once told by an extremely accomplished martial arts expert that there was nothing wrong with running away from a fearful situation, as the only thing that can be damaged is your ego and pride.

Freeze

The third response to fear is to freeze. When applying this to the above scenario, the individual may freeze to the spot where they are standing, not being able to answer the figure, not being able to move. Instead they may stand mute and petrified. Some people who have experienced this fear response report a surreal experience, in which the world appears to slow down. In these circumstances, levels of adrenalin will again be very high.

Fear Responses in Everyday Practice

As a practitioner responsible for the well-being of others, there are many situations where running away is not a valid option. One example of why an individual may experience a fear response when supporting people with behaviours of concern is detailed below:

'Marcus is seven years of age and lives with his mother. When Marcus becomes stressed, he slams doors, shouts and, on some occasions, physically harms his mother and himself. This results in bruising to his mother's arms, legs and torso, in addition to bruises on Marcus's own body. His mother freely admits that she is terrified, and fears for her safety during Marcus's meltdowns. She began using techniques of physical restraint to stop Marcus being able to hurt or injure her (or himself) during these peaks of stress. This often

entailed Marcus being held down on the floor. His mother felt that this was her only option, as she feared what he would do to her, himself or others.'

This example is not unusual. Marcus's mother reduced her own fear by immobilising her son. She was biologically choosing to 'fight' in these circumstances. She certainly couldn't leave a seven-year-old boy to harm himself by choosing to run away. In the animal kingdom, there are very few creatures that submit to being immobilised. Marcus could struggle for up to 10 minutes while being held, during which period screaming obscenities was not unusual. His mother would often tell him to calm down and that she would let go when he was quiet. This created a vicious circle whereby Marcus became calmer after being held so his mum continued to hold him, primarily because she was scared. She eventually realised that this 'trap' was only teaching Marcus to calm down after being forcibly held.

When we are scared, we tend to try to isolate and immobilise people. However, this can lead to people being excessively restrained. This is often a difficult and even paradoxical situation. The more we fear for the safety of others and ourselves, the more we are likely to restrain that individual. Oftentimes, reason that we do this is to protect others or ourselves. With Marcus, his mother reasoned that the use of restraint was to protect them both during his meltdowns as she feared for their safety.

His mother would take him on the ground to restrain him, and before doing so would remove her watch or roll up her sleeves. It is possible that Marcus therefore learnt to fear the removal of a watch or rolling up of sleeves, associating this with restraint occurring. Psychology calls this a conditioned fear response. The more an individual is restrained, the more likely it is that they will experience fear and panic in response to triggering stimuli. There are environments in which vulnerable people witness others being restrained, creating even more trauma. Ultimately, we might think we are managing a situation, but often we are making the individual more fearful and more stressed. As we learned from the stress chapter, increased stress levels will likely lead to the individual displaying more distressed behaviours, thereby increasing the frequency of restraint required.

The Fear of Fear

The very thought of anticipating a fearful situation can lead to a very high fear response even when the situation or thing we fear is not present. This is known as the Fear of Fear Hypothesis (Chambless and Gracely, 1989). This is when the person fears their reaction towards the feeling of fear, and therefore aims to avoid the stimulus or situation that elicits fear before it arises. The fear of fear can be overwhelming and, in some ways, it is often an unhealthy response. Take the example of Marius:

'Marius is a talented Rugby player and very capable carer, but he has a weakness. He experiences a sense of terror when he is exposed unexpectedly to any furry animal. His friends make fun of him about this. He often thinks about furry objects at night, which produces a fear response. The thought processes are a constant reminder that at any time he might see a rat or a dog and become terrified. He avoids places where these creatures are likely to be found. Marius rarely talks about his fear responses as he believes that people might view him as weak. To most people who know Marius, his secret fear is unknown to them.'

Marius had an additional problem when it came to his hidden fear; he was a specialist support worker for children with behaviours of concern. To his colleagues, Marius appeared to be both highly effective and confident when supporting children. In reality, this was an 'illusion' that was difficult to maintain. He found that his fear of everyday furry animals did not appear to apply to his work situations. Ultimately, the difference in fear responses helped him to understand that he was not a 'fearful person' in general. His fear was context-driven, meaning that, in general, he was actually a brave and courageous individual who had a very specific problem. He continues to fulfil his day job without his colleagues ever knowing about his 'phobia'.

Thinking about fearful situations will often be enough to trigger panic attacks. When we are working with people who are highly stressed, it can be difficult to manage our fear. There is a real danger that our fearful thoughts will lead us to take fewer risks with people. This is a human and understandable response. Nonetheless, it can mean that we miss real opportunities to make good emotional connections with people. Identifying safe ways to be in the presence of someone who can scare you is a really important goal:

'Jamie is a seventeen-year-old, twenty stone man, with a form of autism that causes him to struggle to communicate his needs and wishes. Jamie has a reputation for being aggressive, which means that fewer and fewer staff want to work with him. To create a connection with him, Studio3 staff established that, on highly stressed days. it would be safer to manage him outside of his home. Key staff were trained in low arousal approaches and were encouraged to support him in isolated places relatively free of people in order to build up their own confidence. Long walks on beaches

(often in silence) became safe places for them to work. Over time, they learned to 'connect with him' and became less fearful.'

Controlling Our Own Fear

Controlling the biological responses to fear is achievable for many people with practice and time. Some individuals can be attracted to the 'adrenaline rush' - just talk to any individual who climbs rocks or skydives. My colleague, Professor Mark Wetherell at the University of Northumbria, examined cortisol levels before and after skydiving in both experienced and first-time skydivers (Wetherell et al., 2013). He found very little difference in the levels of the stress hormone found in each group. However, the experienced skydivers did appear to report that they felt less stressed. Of course, people who regularly jump out of perfectly good airplanes have to be enjoying the experience to do it more than once. These studies tell us that self-control of our fear does not necessarily make us biologically fearless. Controlling our fear in stressful situations may be much more of an appearance of being calm rather than some 'Zen-like' state.

Fear is Transferable

It is crucial to note at this point that fear is transferable. Thus, not only can you be fearful of the person who is displaying behaviours of concern, but the person displaying distressed behaviour can become fearful themselves. Part of this fear can be due to what is called the transfer of fear, a phenomenon known in psychology as emotional contagion (Elvén, 2010). Fear can spread amongst a staff team very rapidly, and it can lead to fight, flight or freeze responses in support staff. In care situations, fear may be passed on from one person to another without people noticing this exchange occur.

For example, the information we provide about a situation can spread fear. In our field of work, negative information about a person can lead to highly fearful thoughts and feelings towards them. A good example of an everyday phobia is the fear of flying. There are many good reasons why this fear can develop; airplanes are noisy, enclosed environments where people do not have a high sense of control. In addition, human beings are not really designed to fly - this is a modern technological innovation for which we have the Wright brothers to thank. Any situation in which we experience a powerful emotion and do not feel in control can evoke a strong fearful response. It is interesting that one person may find this lack of control liberating, whereas others find it terrifying. Consider the following humorous anecdote:

'Two Studio3 trainers took a short flight home after a long working week. Their training course had been very successful and they were in a positive mood. They watched with the usual disinterest as the flight crew explained the safety drill. They both thought that the demonstration of the use of a life vest was silly. One of them whispered to the other, "You've got very little chance of surviving a high-altitude crash into water. The laws of thermodynamics are pretty clear that it is like a plane hitting a brick wall". They both discussed the idea that the safety routine probably made people more nervous, rather than the intended purpose of making people feel safe and secure. The two trainers were so engrossed in their conversation that they only took notice of the passenger sitting next to them after he ordered two double whiskeys from the drinks trolley during the very short flight. They both felt embarrassed as they realised that he must have heard their childish conversation. The man looked at them and said, "I'm terrified of flying".'

Understanding your own fear is essential if you are to support distressed people in highly fearful situations. For the purpose of this book, we have created a Likert scale questionnaire (similar to the Fear Questionnaire (FQ) used to assess phobias) to establish what elements of working with challenging individuals scares you, and how fearful you currently are in your work.

Think of a person you support or know well who can be described as quite challenging or difficult to work with. Use the following scale to honestly rate situations in which you might want to avoid that person. Remember, avoidance is not necessarily a good thing. Choose a number from the scale below to indicate how often you would avoid each of the situations below because of fear or other unpleasant feelings. Write the number you choose in the space opposite each situation.

1- Never avoid the situation

2- Occasionally avoid the situation

3- Usually avoid the situation

4- Frequently avoid the situation

5- Always avoid the situation

1. Supporting the person with medical treatment (i.e. going to the dentist or doctors)

2. Supporting the person with personal care (i.e. dressing)

3. Supporting the person to eat or drink with other people

4. Travelling with the person in an unfamiliar environment

5. Travelling with the person on public transport

6. Walking with the person on a busy street

7. Going into crowded shops

8. Going into the community

9. The person is hitting or kicking you

10. The person is swearing at you

11. The person is verbally threatening you

12. Watching the person self-harm

13. Being alone at home with them during the day

14. Being alone at home with them during the night

15. Watching the person harming someone else

How Did You Score?

0 to 15: You are probably a person who does not scare easily (or you are in a state of denial!).

16 to 30: You are probably someone who is moderately fearful.

31 to 45: You are probably quite a fearful person.

46 to 60: You are probably a highly fearful person.

61 plus: You are experiencing a state of fear that is unhealthy, and should reflect on your effectiveness in supporting that person.

Even if you scored quite high in the above exercise, try not to be overly worried. Fear can adapt over time and people can adjust quite rapidly. The following describes a positive outcome:

'Jeanette is a thirty-eight-year-old former shop worker who decided that she wanted to change careers and train to be a teacher. To gain experience, she volunteered as a classroom assistant, working with children with autism and what was described as 'severe challenging behaviours'. She received some basic training before being thrown in 'the deep end' by being asked to support a young boy with severe intellectual disabilities and profound communication difficulties. In the space of two months, she received numerous scratches and bruises and two bites on both of her arms whilst changing the young man. In the first month, she had a number of sleepless nights where she was overcome with fear and thoughts of being harmed. She decided to talk to a friend who was a trainee psychotherapist. They offered to emotionally debrief her and provide some guidance. Through this support, Jeannette has learned to 'switch off' from work. She has also developed a better understanding of the young boy. Her confidence increased and her injuries decreased. Having adapted her mindset, she now recognises that she is capable of managing the situation, and has a better relationship with the young boy.'

General Fear

It is quite important to distinguish between fears of a person or situation and our general fears. Fears can be of very specific situations or objects, such as a fear of heights or spiders. However, some individuals appear to have a wide range of general fears, often associated with a fear of harm. The following questionnaire may help you to understand your own general fear.

How do these situations apply to you personally, based on the following scale?

1- Not fearful
2- Slightly fearful
3- Fearful
4- Very fearful
5- Extremely fearful

1) Going to the dentist
2) Someone knocking on your door late at night when you are on your own
3) A stranger threatening to physically harm you
4) Working in a high crime area where there are lots of muggings and crime
5) Being left alone in an unfamiliar area not knowing where you are
6) A stranger threatening you or your family with physical violence
7) Walking through a high crime area late at night
8) Being followed in the street by stranger
9) Watching a fight between two adults
10) A drunken male talking to you at a bus stop
11) A large German Shepherd dog off its lead barking aggressively at you
12) Finding a large rat whilst looking for something in your loft.
13) Getting trapped in a lift on your own
14) Being awoken in your house by the sounds of burglars

15) Needing to have a general anaesthetic for a minor surgical complaint

How Did You Score?

Score 0 to 15: You probably have low generalised fear.

Score 16 to 30: You probably have a mild to moderate state of generalised fear.

Score 31 plus: You may have a high generalised fear state.

Understanding your own generalised and specific fears is essential if you are to become a good low arousal practitioner. Fear is an emotional state that can be difficult to overcome. How we adapt to these fear responses often requires courage, which we will now go on to discuss in more detail.

Courage, Bravery and the Low Arousal Approach

When individuals are scared or fearful, being brave and showing courage is not easy. Courage can be inspiring. In the First World War, Noel Chavasse, a doctor in the Royal Army Medical Corp, won two Victoria Crosses before his sad death in 1917. As an officer, Chavasse believed that he should lead from the front, and routinely went out into 'no man's land' to rescue wounded soldiers. There was little doubt based on his letters that he was experiencing high degrees of fear, yet his desire to help others enabled him to manage this fear. During the tragic events of 9/11, there were many members of the public who behaved heroically. Benjamin Clark, a former marine and chef, according to all accounts behaved calmly and encouraged people in the area to evacuate. He was last seen assisting a person in a wheelchair. What makes people respond so calmly in such obviously distressing situations? One relevant explanation is that individuals such as these are able to focus on the here and now problems, and worry less about the consequences of their actions. We often see people understandably panic, and they engage System 1 thinking in their brain. These are the 'hot processes' that are driven by strong emotions (Kahneman, 2011). Yet, others naturally engage System 2 thinking, and logically react and respond to circumstances. I think that Benjamin Clark's experiences of real-world combat clearly helped him in some way when responding to this crisis. The psychologist Raymond Novaco often referred to the concept of 'stress inoculation' (1977). It means that exposure to stressful situations can lead to increased resilience in some people.

We associate acts of courage with the military, but courage occurs in other areas. Some people, like the late Stephen Hawking, demonstrate extreme courage by living with severe physical disabilities and remaining optimistic. In care situations, staff and parents often show courageous acts daily when supporting individuals who display highly stressed behaviours. Applying the low arousal approach in stressful situations may require a person to be courageous. This is because we may be asking people to avoid responding to conflict and resist their urges to run or fight. Observing a person who is highly distressed can arouse strong feelings within ourselves, but I have found that people can be trained to remain calm in a crisis and appear confident. This was the main reason that my organisation, Studio3, was founded. Of course, this does not mean that we can make everyone courageous. However, we can help them to control their fear in these difficult situations. There are many people who can naturally control their own fear responses, and this does not appear to be related to gender, age, size, weight or any other distinguishing physical characteristic. Understanding and controlling your own fear when faced with distressed individuals is essential in a low arousal approach. I am reminded of a quote from Rudyard Kipling's *If* (1910):

'If you can keep your head when all about you
Are losing theirs and blaming it on you,
If you can trust yourself when all men doubt you,
But make allowance for their doubting too'

Conclusions

Throughout this chapter, we have explored what fear is and why it is a barrier to the low arousal approach. Furthermore, we have discussed the importance of bravery in using the low arousal approach. Bravery can take time to develop, and it is easier said than done. In this case, we advise you to keep trialling the exercise and continue to record your fear score. Your fear score will reduce over time. Fear can often result in an avoidance of confrontation, or it may require us to expose ourselves to risk. In the same way that fear can travel from one person to another, anger is just as contagious an emotion. In stressful situations where we are exposed to anger, we may also experience anger ourselves. That is why understanding the emotion of anger is another crucial component of the low arousal approach.

Key Learning Questions

1) How can fear affect your response to a situation?
2) How does fear affect your body?
3) How does fear transmit from one individual to another?
4) How can you control your own fear?

COPING WITH ANGER

The aim of this chapter is to help practitioners cope with high arousal situations when working in care environments. Being exposed to anger and coping with your own angry responses are an important part of the Low Arousal Approach. In this chapter we will explore what anger is, the different responses to anger, and how to cope with situations that may cause us to feel angry. As with the previous chapters, there is a questionnaire provided for the reader which can be used to investigate your responses to situations that may cause you to feel angry. There are also reflective and practical activities provided which can be used to assist in managing emotions such as anger.

What Is Anger?

Anger, like stress, is neither negative or positive. Anger has survival value and is an emotion that can be helpful to us in certain situations (Rodgers, 2014). It is important to understand that anger in controlled circumstances may have positive as well as negative elements.

Clausen (2007) defined anger as an emotional state that can range in intensity from mild irritation to intense fury and rage. Anger has negative connotations but is, in essence, the emotional expression of a biological response such as increased heart rate, blood pressure and adrenaline. Anger can be triggered by external or internal threat, and can make people 'less analytical and more reflective in [their] decisions' (Sapolsky, 2017: p.62).

Anger is a natural physiological and psychological response to a perceived threat, either to the self or to important others, present, past or future. The threat may appear to be real, discussed, or imagined. Oftentimes, the threat is due to a physical conflict, injustice, negligence, humiliation or betrayal, amongst other contentions (Clausen, 2007). Therefore, when we feel threatened, highly stressed or highly aroused, the expression of anger becomes more likely. The experience of anger can be individual (a person directs their anger at you) or it can be collective (an angry crowd of football fans screaming abuse at opposing fans).

Anger is much more common than we are inclined to imagine. Psychologists are becoming increasingly aware of the emotional damage of exposure to anger. When children are exposed to aggressive behaviour or anger between their parents, it can have long-term psychological implications (Heitler, 2018). Contrary to what we might believe, anger is a frequently occurring emotion, the moderate to intense forms of which may be experienced several times a day by any given individual. In addition, angry thoughts are far more common than angry behaviours. Consider the following example:

'Yasmin is a twenty-five-year-old support worker who spends a great deal of her time with children who have special needs. Yasmin is known to be quite calm and efficient in her work. She recently completed a training course in managing the emotional responses of children, through the course of which she realised that she was 'quite angry' when she travelled to and from work in her car. These angry thoughts and behaviours took the form of shouting at other drivers from the safety of her car. Her anger seemed only to occur in this context and did not seem to affect her work.'

In Yasmin's situation, her anger is context-driven. She is not described by her colleagues as some kind of 'Incredible Hulk' figure, constantly on the verge of anger. Instead, her anger is focused on one specific context. This could be described as a normal profile for everyday anger.

Monitoring Your Own and Other People's Everyday Anger

To understand anger in other people, it is useful to begin by considering your own experience of anger. It is also important to distinguish between angry thoughts and openly angry behaviours. Answer the following questions as honestly as possible:

> 1) In the last week, how many angry thoughts have you had about a person or a situation?

2) How intense are these angry thoughts? (Do they persist, are they repetitive?)

3) Have you been openly angry with someone in the last week?

4) How intense are these angry behaviours?

5) Have you witnessed a person being angry in the last week?

The above exercise is an easy way to identify anger-related behaviours in our daily lives. How often have you felt angry today, and how intensely did you feel this emotion? It is important that people are a little less judgemental about their experience of everyday anger, and are aware that anger is a natural part of our lives. It is impossible to eradicate anger from our toolkit of human emotions. However, being able to resolve angry emotions when they occur is essential.

There are a wide range of potential triggers for anger. Novaco (2000) reported that anger is evoked by a variety of external factors (e.g. persons, objects, and situations) or internal sensations (e.g. anger-laden memories, feelings of rejection, humiliation, and anxiety) that are interpreted as provocative and wrongful. Take some time to think about what sort of things make you angry. These things may well be things that are universal triggers for anger, or they may be specific to your life and experiences. The expression of anger varies across cultures, but there are some very common factors. Take a look at the following list and identify what applies to you:

a)   Road rage

b)   People cutting in front of you in queues

c)   The weather

d)   Someone being rude to you

e)   Your biscuit falling into your mug of tea or coffee

f)   Someone taking the last item you wanted to buy in a shop

g)   Your sports team losing in an important match

h)   Someone taking advantage of you

Being aware of our own angry triggers is essential in our work, and also encourages us to be more aware of when the people we support are more likely to have an angry response.

Exposure to Anger

Being exposed to anger on a daily basis can be difficult to manage, especially when supporting distressed individuals:

'Jason supports his elderly mother, Mary, at home. Mary's Alzheimer's disease leads to memory problems and explosive bouts of anger. In her former career, Mary had been a school teacher and rarely used bad language of any kind. In the present situation, she often swears and shouts at her son, accusing him of stealing money. Mary's intense rages seem to last for hours.'

Even though Jason stated that he could cope with his mother's behaviour, he sometimes finds the situation overwhelming. In these circumstances, Jason is not in a position to control these situations. Everyday anger that is difficult to control can be upsetting, as well as debilitating and even embarrassing. For example:

'Emma and Tom have an eighteen-month-old girl called Gemmima. In recent weeks, her nursery teachers have identified 3 occasions in which Gemmima bit another child. Both parents believe that this is just a phase, but still experience huge embarrassment that their reasonably well-behaved child can do such a thing.'

Inability to control a young child's anger is a terrible situation for parents. They will often feel judged by their peers as being 'bad parents' for being unable to control their child. Although the teaching staff were quite accepting of the 'mystifying situation', her parents continued to be embarrassed. First, because they could not understand why the behaviour was happening and second, they were aware of the 'knowing looks' from other parents. Sometimes to resolve these issues we simply have to accept that we cannot always explain every single behaviour that occurs.

How We Express Anger

How we express our anger can be especially pertinent; for example, whether it is done through active or passive emotion and behaviours. In the case of 'active' emotion, the angry person 'lashes out' verbally or physically at an intended target. When anger is a 'passive' emotion, it is characterised by silent sulking, passive-aggressive behaviour (hostility) and tension (Clausen, 2007). How we view the situation can have a significant impact on how we react and respond. Consider the following example, and ask yourself how you would respond in this situation:

'You are in an emergency department waiting to be seen by a doctor. A man stumbles into the department. He appears to be drunk and looks quite dishevelled. He approaches the receptionist and begins to shout, demanding to be seen by a doctor straight away. He is told

that there is a queue and that he must take a number and wait to be seen by a nurse first. The man becomes even angrier, and begins to hurl verbal abuse at the receptionist. A nurse intervenes, taking him to a side room in order to get him out of the reception area. She politely and calmly walks up to him and says, "Sir, I can see you in here". Some of the people in the waiting room appear to become annoyed that this man is going to be seen first.'

How you would feel? Many people who had been patiently waiting in the department would question why the man was seen before them. Why did he get seen so quickly and not have to wait in the queue as they had? The answer is quite simple; the hospital staff had to divert him away from the group of people watching and becoming uncomfortable. They were essentially adopting a low arousal approach. If the hospital staff had not intervened, someone else might have engaged the man in a similarly aggressive manner. Would you have intervened? What action would you have chosen to take, and how angry would you have felt whilst doing this? Would this have resolved the issue?

Does knowledge of the person help us to understand their aggressive and angry behaviours? Let us think about the information we have been given in the example and see if more knowledge of the man would help us to empathise with him or not. Consider the following; would you still feel angry in the situation now that you have the following additional information?

1)   The man is well-known to the medical staff and has an alcohol problem.

YES   NO   NOT SURE

2) The man is a known violent criminal.

YES   NO   NOT SURE

3) The receptionist seems really calm.

YES   NO   NOT SURE

4) The receptionist starts to cry.

YES   NO   NOT SURE

5) The people in the waiting room are starting to shout at him to be quiet.

YES   NO   NOT SURE

6) The receptionist wants a low-key response and has already indicated that security should be called.

YES   NO   NOT SURE

7) The man has had a really stressful day and has been drinking because he has found out that his best friend suddenly passed away.

YES   NO   NOT SURE

8) The man has type 2 Diabetes and has drank no alcohol, but is confused due to not taking his routine medication.

YES   NO   NOT SURE

9) The man was a former soldier who suffers from PTSD.

YES   NO   NOT SURE

10)   A pregnant mother in the waiting room begins to sob uncontrollably.

YES   NO   NOT SURE

11)   There are many young children in the waiting room.

YES   NO   NOT SURE

12)   The person has a carving knife.

YES   NO   NOT SURE

Take a look at your answers and explore which of these factors would have an impact on you.

It is really important to try and understand why people become angry. However, when managing a situation, the path of least resistance is often the best way. In many ways, it does not matter what the reasons are for the man's distress - removing him from the situation and the onlookers will potentially reduce the chance of confrontation and increased arousal. Coping with anger that is directly targeted towards you is a very difficult situation. In care environments, people can be exposed to anger in a wide variety of settings. Supporters, families and carers of individuals who present with behaviours of concern can be faced with anger on a regular basis. The impact of this can be hard to manage, but first you must be able to accept that you feel angry.

Being Honest About Anger

When we experience extreme behaviours, including being physically assaulted, there is a tendency to deny the emotional experience that inevitably accompanies the physical. This can be damaging, as our emotional responses can impact how we choose to physically and verbally resolve the situation. For example, in Spanish culture, men are sometimes referred to as 'Macho', a stereotype that can influence their behaviour in stressful situations:

'Torbjorn is an eighteen-year-old student who was mugged by three young men on his way home from university. The three men attacked him physically, pulling him to the ground, kicking and punching him, stealing his wallet and running away. Torbjorn did not tell his friends about the incident at first, as he felt embarrassed that he had not managed to defend himself. He tells people who ask that he is 'fine'. In truth, he is angry about the incident and very angry with himself.'

Saying that you are 'fine' when you most certainly are not can be a real problem, especially when supporting vulnerable individuals. In care environments, how we respond to people requires emotional honesty. Lundström, Aström and Graneheim (2007) interviewed staff who had been assaulted by the people they supported, and found that after exposure to violence they either experienced sensations of emotionally 'falling apart' or 'keeping it together'. Admitting anger is an important first step towards forgiveness and resolution, which can only be achieved by facing the emotional trauma that can follow violent and aggressive incidents. It is also important for professionals to be positive role models, which means modelling forgiveness and recognising when we may have acted out of anger or fear. The late Albert Kushlick, a Psychiatrist and an inspirational voice in the UK in the 1970s and 1980s, had a very practical approach to supporting people by encouraging them to acknowledge their fears (personal communication, 1992). He argued that people tend to over-control behaviours, which can be unhealthy. Most importantly, Kushlick argued that staff needed to change their view of behaviours. We may strive to be more like Kushlick, but inspirational leaders know that emotions such as anger can spread as easily as fear.

An Attributional Bias Exercise

Interpreting everyday situations can lead to assumptions being made, which in turn cause angry responses. We know that the brain has at least two types of processing systems, according to Daniel Kahneman (2011). Read the following four situations and reflect carefully about your answers.

'At the Supermarket'

Part 1

You are doing your shopping at a local supermarket. It is quite busy, and as you approach the checkout aisles you see two people arguing. They are gesturing wildly towards each other and their voices are raised. As you draw nearer, you can hear that one person has accused the other of jumping the queue. You don't know either of them and they are complete strangers to you.

What would you do in this situation? Would you intervene? Or leave them to argue and purchase your items? Try to be honest with your answers. Most people would state that they would probably not say anything in this situation.

Part 2

You are doing your shopping at a local supermarket. It is quite busy, and as you approach the checkout aisles you see two people arguing. They are gesturing wildly towards each other and their voices are raised. As you draw nearer, you recognise one of the voices and see that it is someone you know.

What would you do in this situation? Would you help the person you know and resolve the argument? Or leave them to argue and purchase your items? Many people would say that, in this situation, they would probably intervene and show support for the person they knew.

Part 3

You are doing your shopping at a local supermarket. It is quite busy, and as you approach the checkout aisles you see two people arguing. They are gesturing wildly towards each other and their voices are raised. As you draw nearer, you can see that one person is a wheelchair user.

What would you do in this situation? Would you help to resolve the argument? Or leave them to argue and purchase your items? Would you help the wheelchair user or the able-bodied person? Would you decide that the person in the wheelchair is more vulnerable, and therefore deserving of help?

Part 4

You are doing your shopping at a local supermarket. It is quite busy, and as you approach the checkout aisles you see two people arguing. They are gesturing wildly towards each other and their voices are raised. As you draw nearer, you can see that both people are dressed very shabbily, are unshaven, and smell of alcohol.

What would you do in this situation? Would you help either of these people? Would you help to resolve the argument, or leave them to argue and purchase your items?

This exercise is designed to demonstrate how unconsciously we make very quick assessments about people on a daily basis, based on how much or how little information is available to us. Try to reflect on when you would act and when you would not, and what this tells you about your own empathy levels towards angry behaviour. We naturally make snap judgements - sometimes instantaneously and without much considered thought. We act upon our first instincts, which can sometimes be full of biases, affecting whether we intervene or not. Social psychological studies into bystander intervention have consistently demonstrated that people will usually only help a person who seems to be having a heart attack if other people are also helping (Darley and Latane, 1968). In a series of studies, the 'helping' behaviour of members of the public was tested experimentally by actors (ibid., 1970). They observed that the more bystanders present to witness an actor apparently having a heart attack, the less likely people were to intervene. They also found that the smell of alcohol on a person's clothing increased the likelihood that people would ignore their need for help. On a positive note, some people did intervene quickly, which then encouraged other people to help. These studies tell us that we make rapid decisions in situations, and that these decisions are influenced by our social environment. The next time you see someone in trouble, remember to take the lead and ask them if they are OK - if you walk on by, others will too.

Angry People Make Poor Decisions

In our day-to-day work supporting people who are distressed, we may often find ourselves involved in making decisions about risk and safety. Our own emotional framework can greatly influence this process. This is especially true if people are not aware of their own emotional state. For example:

THE REFLECTIVE JOURNEY

'Nathan is a fourteen-year-old boy with a traumatised past. He regularly disrupts classroom lessons by swearing and shouting. His teachers were becoming increasingly irritated and annoyed by his defiance. They called an emergency meeting and agreed upon a tough set of sanctions in order to get him to conform. These ultimately appeared to escalate his behaviour.'

In this example, there was a disconnect between the staff and the pupil. They were angry with the young man, but blissfully unaware that this was driving their behaviour. There are a series of studies which demonstrate that anger-fuelled decision-making is far less efficient, and may lead us to consider punishment in many circumstances (Sapolsky, 2017). Anger-related decision making is an area of concern within a low arousal approach, and requires people to be reflective practitioners. It is important to stress that anger is an emotion that can be contagious, especially if a person's behaviours of concern are extreme in nature. To be a good low arousal practitioner, you need to be able to identify and recognise your own anger. A simple rule is to follow Mind's (a UK mental health charity) three simple steps for controlling anger (2013):

1) Look out for the early signs of anger.

2) Give yourself time and space to process the triggers.

3) Apply techniques to help you control the anger.

Whether we are fearful or angry, we must always reflect that this will affect our view of other people's behaviours. Both of these emotions can sometimes lead to us believe that people are trying to control us. This in turn can cause us to become over-controlling towards others.

The next chapter will examine the battle for control that can exist between individuals and their supporters.

Key Learning Questions

1) What is anger?

2) How do you recognise your own anger?

3) Think of ways that you could reduce your own anger in a crisis situation.

4) What do we mean when we say that anger is 'contagious'? Think of a time when anger has spread from one person to another.

THE BATTLE FOR CONTROL

One of the lesser-known human needs is the need for control. Human beings inherently desire a sense of control in their lives but why is this so? Some may believe that being able to control our everyday environment leads to a more positive sense of well-being. More control of the physical environment may have an evolutionary advantage, as there would be fewer immediate threats and danger to our safety. In the modern world, this still applies, but many would argue that the need for perceived control is greater. Most people would agree that we all have a need to control our world, and that this is especially important for people who are highly distressed.

What is Perceived Control and Why is it Important?

Studies have shown that having a greater belief that you are in control can have better outcomes for job satisfaction, health and well-being. A recent UK survey into the lives of people with learning disabilities identified serious health inequalities, leading to shorter life expectations of around 15-20 years (Marmot et al., 2017). Although this evidence is correlational, it supports a huge body of research which suggests that there is a relationship between our perceived level of control over our lives and our health outcomes.

There is evidence that the more actual control you have over your working life, the better your health outcomes. In the UK, a series of classic studies known as the Whitehall studies (named after the headquarters of the British Civil Service in Whitehall) demonstrated a clear link between mortality and level of employment hierarchy, in that there was a higher mortality rate for people who were lower down in the hierarchy (ibid., 1997). The Whitehall II study, conducted twenty years later showed a similar social gradient in mortality rates, as well as the prevalence of a number of illnesses in people lower down the economic hierarchy (ibid., 2015). Whilst economic factors obviously contribute to these results, other studies have shown that quality of life is greatly affected by choice and perceived control. One of the most important longitudinal studies of aging, dementia and psychological well-being are the Nun Studies. One particular study strongly links positive emotional statements from young nuns writing about their vocation with lower rates of mortality in later life (Danmer and Freison, 2001). This suggests that having a positive outlook and perceived control over your life and work can actually lead to greater physical well-being.

The idea that our psychological make-up can be a factor in such results is rather surprising. In many care situations, there are often strong debates about allowing individuals to make decisions and choices, and in essence giving people more 'actual' control over their lives. The low arousal approach has an extremely strong focus on the importance of perceived control for individuals who are highly distressed. Our well-being is linked to our ability to exercise a certain degree of control over our lives. To put it simply, if we believe that we have more control over our lives, our health and well-being will be better.

Are You a Control Freak?

Have you ever been called a control freak? Think about how much control you have in your daily life. Are there certain aspects of life that you have a need to be in control of? Alternatively, are there certain aspects of life that you are not too fussed about, where you would prefer others to take the lead?

The following simple questions encourage the reader to think about how important control is in their lives. Think about some of the day-to-day activities below, and reflect on how much control you would like to have:

Who holds the remote control whilst you are choosing a programme to watch on TV?
If it is you, why? How would you feel if you were not able to hold it? If someone else holds the remote, does it matter who this person is? Would you feel more or less comfortable knowing your partner is holding the remote?

Who decides what you will eat for dinner?

If it is you, how do you make this choice? Do you take into consideration your food likes and dislikes? Do you take into consideration others' food likes and dislikes? If it is someone else, how do you know what they will choose to cook? Does not knowing make you feel like you need to ask them?

Who chose the colour of the walls in your home?

If it was you, how did you reach this decision? Was it a solo or joint decision? If it was not you, do you feel you are able to change the colour if you wanted to?

Which side of the bed did you choose to sleep on?

If you chose, how did you come to this decision? If someone else chose, are you happy with the side you sleep on? What would happen if you chose to sleep on the opposite side tonight?

Do you have a set routine regarding how you get ready in the morning?

If yes, how did you come to develop this routine? If no, would you be willing to develop one and follow it rigidly? Would you be willing to swap your morning routine with someone else's and follow it strictly?

Try to reflect on how these questions made you feel about your perceived sense of control. Are you open to changes? Are you able to manage when others take the lead in some areas of life? Or do you feel the need to be the person who leads in these areas? Does the idea of someone else taking the lead fill you with dread?

When we are supporting individuals who are highly distressed, it is nearly always the case that those people will seek to control their immediate environment. In essence, they are trying to simplify their world and make it appear less chaotic and unpredictable. Take the following situation for example:

'Emily is a thirty-two-year-old shop manager who, over the years, has had issues around her weight. When she was sixteen, she was given a formal diagnosis of anorexia nervosa. Since her early adulthood, she has managed to control her eating effectively. She observed that the more stressed she became, the more powerful the urges to control what she ate. She described this to her therapist as 'the only thing she can control'. Recently she received a promotion at work, resulting in her stress level being elevated. Over time, Emily learned that, instead of attempting to control her eating, she found it much more positive to control other things in her life. She has developed cleaning rituals and very subtle touching rituals which she believes are far less negative in their impact on her life than controlling her eating.'

Emily demonstrates that a sense of control can be achieved in positive ways. Her eating disorder served the clear function of giving her a sense of control over her life, even though it was incredibly damaging to her. Having a sense of control over our lives is essential for us to thrive.

How Much Control Do the People We Support Have On a Day-to-Day Basis?

It is the sad reality that many of the people we support will have experienced occasions where they were not able to control areas of their lives that they would have liked to. Think about an individual you work with - how much choice and control do they have in their lives? Who makes decisions about what they watch, what they eat and where they sleep? How much control do they have over their environments, routines and activities? The more distressed people become, the more important even basic, everyday routines become.

Over-Control and Excessive Use of Rules and Boundaries

When someone is distressed, the need for them to feel in control is extremely important. As someone becomes more stressed, their world becomes more and more narrow until they feel as though they can only control themselves by controlling the world around them. Supporting someone in times of heightened stress to regain a sense of control is fundamental. The support we provide, however, will be influenced by how we view others. The late Albert Kushlick argued that people tend to over-control behaviours and that, in order to prevent this, staff need to view behaviours as being less wilful and deliberate (Kushlick et al., 1997). Therefore, it is not just the person we are supporting's perception of control that is important, but also our own perception of that person's control. I have been strongly influenced in this work by clinical psychologist Professor Dave Dagnan. He has long held the view that perception of behaviour is a crucial factor in well-being. Dave has a unique ability to develop simple, everyday measures that can be incredibly useful in real-life settings. I was involved in developing the controllability beliefs scale with him and his colleagues (Dagnan et al., 2004; 2013).

The Controllability Beliefs Scale

Do you believe that a person is fully in control of their behaviour? Do you think that they are attempting to control you? The more you view the person as being in control, the less likely it is that you will want to help them. This principle is based on a model developed by the psychologist Bernard Weiner (1980). The following questionnaire has been designed to help the reader understand how they think about behaviour, and the kinds of attributions that they make.

Think about an individual you work with or have worked with who displays behaviours of concern. Focus on one behaviour of concern in particular that you often encounter. Listed below are thoughts that you may have had when supporting this person. Think about each statement and tick the relevant box to indicate how much you agree with each statement.

THE REFLECTIVE JOURNEY
The Thoughts About Challenging Behaviour Questionnaire:

Statements:	Agree Strongly	Agree slightly	Unsure	Disagree Slightly	Disagree strongly
1.He/she is trying to wind me up*					
2.He/she can't help themselves					
3.He/she is doing it deliberately*					
4.He/she knows what they are doing*					
5.He/she has no control over their behaviour					

6.He/she could stop if they wanted*					
7.He/she is trying to manipulate the situation*					
8.He/she can think through their actions*					
9.He/she doesn't mean to upset people					
10.He/she is in control of their own behaviour*					

11.He/she means to make me feel bad*					
12.He/she has chosen to behave in this way*					
13.He/she is not to blame for what they do					
14.He/she knows the best time to challenge*					
15. He/she doesn't realise how it makes me feel					

Scoring is quite simple. To help you here is a simple guide: there are 10 answers with an asterisk (*). These answers make up your score and are ranked as follows: strongly agree equals 5 points, agree equals 4 points, undecided equals 3 points, disagree equals 2 points and strongly disagree equals 1 point.

Add the scores from these 10 questions for a maximum score of 50 and a minimum score of 10.

What Was Your Score?

35 to 50 - You have a high perception of control and may view many behaviours of concern as deliberate and wilful. This may make you less empathic towards individuals.

20 to 34 - You have a moderate perception of control and sometimes struggle to view behaviours as controlling. You fluctuate in your views of behaviours of concern.

10 to 19 - You have a low controllability beliefs score and your general view is that many behaviours are not under the person's control. You are more likely to be empathic towards people who show behaviours of concern.

Controllability is a continuum for many people. There are many situations in which we may be in control of our behaviour because of social rules. We have laws that we try to follow and rules that, when they are broken, have consequences. Self-control and self-regulation are therefore an important part of our lives. Developing self-control is dependent on both our own emotional and cognitive development, and the external environment. A society without any rules and boundaries would be anarchic in nature. The reality is that, under high states of stress, we may lose control. A good example of this is when we have arguments with people. You may have a dispute with a person that leads to an argument and increased arousal. In these circumstances, you may lose control and not process information in a logical manner. Emotional or 'hot processes' can lead to explosive behaviour.

Think back to the chapter on anger, where we described a scenario in which two people were arguing in the supermarket when you were shopping. If we perceive someone as being aware and in control of their behaviour, how would we respond to this? Now compare this to how we would respond if we see the person as not being in control and unaware of their behaviour. Thus, how aware and in control *perceive* the person to be impacts how we react and respond to that. Think about the people you support. Where in the 'control matrix' would you place them? No one is truly 100% in control of their behaviour all of the time, therefore there should be methods of responding to distressed behaviour that have everyone's best interests at heart.

Now that we have established that our perceptions of control may have an impact on our own behaviour, we must begin to think about behaviours of concern as people we support losing control due to 'hot' emotional processing. The belief that a person is totally in control of their behaviour can lead to serious negative consequences. When we work with people who display behaviours of concern, it can be tempting to think that they are in control of their behaviours. As a result, we can be tempted to use punitive methods in order to change that behaviour.

Perceived Control: Sanctions, Consequences and Punishment

When we believe that a person is in control of their behaviour, we can often overuse methods of control in order to change the behaviour. Sanctions and consequences are frequently used to establish control over behaviours. American psychologist B. F. Skinner pioneered the idea that behaviour is often shaped by reinforcement (Ferster and Skinner, 1957). Therefore, a reinforced consequence can lead to a behaviour increasing in frequency. However, reinforcement is a strange thing, defined by its impact. Positively reinforcing a person's behaviour by praising them or using rewards will only work if those consequences are relevant to the person. In addition, negative reinforcement is often misunderstood. If reinforcement makes a behaviour more likely to occur, negative reinforcement means removing something that reinforces behaviour. For example, in care settings, avoidance can become a negative reinforcer.

The problem with using negative or positive reinforcement to change behaviour is that behaviours are complex and not usually linked to simple consequences. Many of the vulnerable people we support have at some point been victims of what can only be described as 'negative behaviour support'. They have often been subjected to therapies which do not focus on positive reinforcement. Instead, they have focused on the withdrawal of privileges, the use of sanctions and enforcement of negative consequences. In psychological terms, if you add something to or remove something from a situation and it reduces or suppresses behaviour, then according to behaviourists you are using a form of punishment. It is easy to see why some people turn to these methods when they are fearful of extreme behaviours: it is not unusual that frightened people will attempt to exert more control over the things that they are scared of. It is true that these approaches can suppress behaviours if they are severe enough. However, there are many problems with using these methods over a prolonged period of time, as they often damage relationships and cause resentment towards supporters.

There are also many circumstances in which punishment may lead to people becoming even more angry. Think about a time when you might have been punished by a teacher or a parent. How accepting were you of the punishment? Why are these approaches so attractive to some, and overused when working with people who are distressed? The simple answer is that in highly fear-evoking situations we try to assert control, often claiming that the 'ends justify the means'. The Judge Rotenberg Center in the US routinely used electric shock devices to control aggressive behaviour in children (Pilkington, 2018). This highly controversial approach was justified by staff who claimed that punishment was effective. I accept that this is an extreme example of the use of punishment, however it does show how easily controlling methods can become very attractive for people. The paradox is that for punishing or negative consequences to work, the person must be able to control their own behaviour. The more we perceive a person as being in control of their behaviour, the more likely we are to intervene using punitive consequences. This view fails to acknowledge the fact that some behaviours are not necessarily always under our control.

For example, weight loss and gain are very good examples of behaviours which we perceive as being totally under our own control. Our society has been described as 'obesogenic'; that is, we exist in a fast food, low exercise culture which leads some people to become addicted to junk food. There are also biological and social factors that can affect a person's control over their own behaviour. It may well be true that a person who is not classified as obese is able to lose weight, but when people become morbidly obese, they are, in reality, addicted to food. Asking a person who eats compulsively to control their eating, or reducing their self-esteem by telling them that it is easy to lose weight is unhelpful. Punishment is an engrained part of our society which it assumes that negative consequences alter behaviour. Research tends to suggest that punishment only works up to a point. In the UK in 2018, we put 92,500 people in prison (Sturge, 2018). Yet, according to government statistics, reoffending rates are very high, with 48% of adult prisoners reoffending within one year of being released (Prison Reform Trust, 2018). These statistics also show that many people who serve prison sentences for violent crimes are often drug users (O'Hagan, 2017). Punishing addicts within the judicial system seems to represent the spirit of overcontrol in our society. We may believe that it is effective, but the reality is that, without proper rehabilitation, drug addicts are likely to reoffend. This calls into question how effective prisons really are, and whether they are centres for reform or simply a way of removing people from society for prolonged periods of time.

Withdrawing rewards from people is also a controversial method of behaviour management. Consider the following example:

'Iain is a twenty-two-year-old man recently recovering from a psychotic episode in a medium secure facility. Iain's behaviour has been erratic and sometimes violent towards staff. The behavioural programme adopted on the ward is based on earning incentives. However, there is also a punishment element, namely that if he misbehaves, he will have his rewards deducted. This is a little contradictory, as it assumes that he has the ability to control his aggressive behaviour. The use of incentives and disincentives has a limited effect on Iain. It has been noted that his behaviour will escalate in the presence of senior staff members who often impose

these sanctions. The programme continued with little effect for over two years. '

Why are Iain's staff so addicted to a strategy that is clearly not working? The answer lies in the need for people to control others in the name of 'safety'. Once we start to overuse sanctions and boundaries, it damages the therapeutic relationship between individuals and their supporters. People may become angry or withdrawn, and fail to build positive, trusting relationships with their supporters. Even more worryingly, every time we use methods which assert our control, we fail to encourage the person we are supporting to develop self-control of their own. The arguments for punishment are manifold, but they have no place within a low arousal framework where we are supporting people who are highly distressed. The old adage is useful here: 'Don't add fuel to the fire'. In this approach, negotiation will always be more effective than methods of control, and, of course, more humane.

'Natural consequences' is a term often used by people in support roles, meaning that consequences of behaviours must occur for learning to take place. There are many natural consequences to acts. If a person is upset and refusing to engage in an activity that they like, the natural consequence may well be that they do not engage in that activity. Even if this is considered by people to be a more gentle approach, there is a danger that it can also be overused. For example, a person who does not take their epilepsy medication may have the natural consequence of a seizure. It is true that people often make poor life decisions, and, to a certain extent, it is essential that we learn from these lest we repeat our old mistakes.

There are times when we may need to 'ride out the storm'. In these circumstances, the use of medication, at least in the short-term, should always be a strong consideration. In the next section we will discuss this issue in more detail.

Use of Medication to Control People

In care settings of all kinds, the use of psychotropic medication is very commonplace. There is a place for medications in care settings, but if supporters are strongly medically-minded they will often be inclined to view medication as an intervention, and fail to consider less invasive, non-medication alternatives first. I once worked with an eminent psychiatrist in the intellectual disability field who was attempting to avoid the use of medication by only using it as a last resort. The following example illustrates the importance of treating medication as a last stop when managing behaviours of concern:

'A Studio3 clinician was asked to review a person with intellectual disabilities living in a low security environment. Although the staff team had managed this man pretty well for the last year, his stress had accumulated in recent weeks, leading to an incident where he had physically grabbed a member of staff with two hands around their throat, yelling, "If you don't shut up, I'll kill you!" The staff member was very frightened, and her fear spread to other members of the team. They called an emergency review to discuss the prospect of increasing his medication. After a highly emotional meeting, the psychiatrist decided to increase the man's medication. Later, he confided that he felt this medication alteration was 'insignificant', effective only in the sense that it gave the staff team a sense of control over the situation. He also stated that 'he wished he could have persuaded them that the status quo was probably enough'. He

believed very strongly that the medically-minded staff team had resorted to medical interventions far too rapidly.'

In this case, an isolated but obviously terrifying incident resulted in the prescription of medication that was probably not necessary. The man's outburst was clearly a result of elevated stress, which was most likely linked to a change in his environment. By tackling the external stress triggers in the man's environment, a future incident could have been avoided. However, the staff no longer felt in control, and felt safer using medication than taking the risk of another incident occurring.

How Pharmacologically Minded Are You?

When we think that a person we support is not in control, we naturally think of medications to help them re-gain control. My colleague Gary McKenna, who is now a trainee clinical psychologist in Galway in the Republic of Ireland, developed a simple questionnaire that focuses on people's view of pharmacological interventions (McKenna et al., 2015). In order to gauge and reflect on your view of pharmacological interventions, please complete the questionnaire below.

THE REFLECTIVE JOURNEY

Please circle the response that most accurately and honestly reflects your opinion:

1. Non-pharmacological interventions should be used more often than they are currently used when responding to behaviours of concern*

Strongly Disagree	Disagree	Somewhat Disagree	Undecided	Somewhat Agree	Agree	Strongly Agree
1	2	3	4	5	6	7

2. Non-pharmacological interventions should be used before pharmacological ones when responding to behaviours of concern+

Strongly Disagree	Disagree	Somewhat Disagree	Undecided	Somewhat Agree	Agree	Strongly Agree
1	2	3	4	5	6	7

3. In my response to behaviours of concern, I address the etiology of the behaviours

Strongly Disagree	Disagree	Somewhat Disagree	Undecided	Somewhat Agree	Agree	Strongly Agree
1	2	3	4	5	6	7

4. Psychotropic medication is the last resort when treating people with autism and behaviours of concern+

Strongly Disagree	Disagree	Somewhat Disagree	Undecided	Somewhat Agree	Agree	Strongly Agree
1	2	3	4	5	6	7

5. For many behaviours of concern, there are no pharmacological interventions

Strongly Disagree	Disagree	Somewhat Disagree	Undecided	Somewhat Agree	Agree	Strongly Agree
1	2	3	4	5	6	7

6. Psychotropic medication works well for behaviours of concern*

Strongly Disagree	Disagree	Somewhat Disagree	Undecided	Somewhat Agree	Agree	Strongly Agree
1	2	3	4	5	6	7

7. Most behaviours of concern cannot be handled by behavioural or non-pharmacological interventions

Strongly Disagree	Disagree	Somewhat Disagree	Undecided	Somewhat Agree	Agree	Strongly Agree
1	2	3	4	5	6	7

8. Pharmacological intervention is far more important than non-pharmacological intervention*

Strongly Disagree	Disagree	Somewhat Disagree	Undecided	Somewhat Agree	Agree	Strongly Agree
1	2	3	4	5	6	7

9. Staff request medication too quickly, and more often than it is really needed

Strongly Disagree	Disagree	Somewhat Disagree	Undecided	Somewhat Agree	Agree	Strongly Agree
1	2	3	4	5	6	7

10. There are insufficient resources to use non-pharmacological interventions*

Strongly Disagree	Disagree	Somewhat Disagree	Undecided	Somewhat Agree	Agree	Strongly Agree
1	2	3	4	5	6	7

11. I believe that staff do not seek to use a non-pharmacological intervention prior to using medication

Strongly Disagree	Disagree	Somewhat Disagree	Undecided	Somewhat Agree	Agree	Strongly Agree
1	2	3	4	5	6	7

12. Staff members do not know how to intervene non-pharmacologically for behaviours of concern

Strongly Disagree	Disagree	Somewhat Disagree	Undecided	Somewhat Agree	Agree	Strongly Agree
1	2	3	4	5	6	7

13. Many behaviours of concern stem from staff not paying attention to the service user's needs

Strongly Disagree	Disagree	Somewhat Disagree	Undecided	Somewhat Agree	Agree	Strongly Agree
1	2	3	4	5	6	7

Since this is a controversial topic, it is difficult to score someone as being pharmacologically minded or not. When you have completed this questionnaire, we have marked some of the questions with either a *, which means that you are probably more pharmacologically minded if you agree strongly, and others with a +, which suggests that you are less pharmacologically minded if you agree with these statements. Some questions are deliberately unclassified. Rather than scoring this statistically, please now reflect on your answers, and ask yourself what this tells you about your own beliefs on behaviours being controlled by medication.

Medication has a place in our line of work, but the more pharmacologically minded you are, the more likely you are to use and request medications for crisis management. We may often witness a person appear to be calmer after administration of medication, which then reinforces the belief that the medication is working. This may not be the case, as the following example demonstrates:

'A staff team in an acute psychiatric service are taking part in a reflective practice seminar, and having an extensive debate about the role of psychotropic medication. In particular, they are discussing the use of emergency medication for highly distressed individuals, many of whom have been detained for their own safety. They decided *to examine the use of emergency medication in the form of injections, which was relatively rare, by examining the data from the previous year. It is clear that this is a highly empathic group of individuals, who often feel guilty about administering such medications. One member of staff commented that they only did this in extreme situations, and that there was no other option but to restrain people in order to give the injection. They found that, in a significant number of instances, the period of time reported for a calming effect to occur was far too rapid for the drug to have been the root cause. They also noticed that more females than males over the year received this medication.'*

This example shows the complexities of such situations. After this evaluation, the psychiatric team came to believe that once the injection was delivered, staff who believed in its calming effect would let go of the person and withdraw to a safe distance. The ritual of administering the injection, although unpleasant, allowed staff to calm down and gave them a sense of being in control of the situation. In reality, it was probably this withdrawal of restraint and release of tension in the staff members that led to the person being injected beginning to calm down. In my experience, stressed and sometimes frightened people will seek quick solutions to a crisis, and unfortunately, unnecessary medication is often one such solution. However, there are circumstances in which medication can be valuable.

Who Requires Medication?

Medication can either be supportive to a person's well-being or imposed on them in order to control their behaviour. I once worked with an eminent UK psychiatrist (now retired) who told me that psychotropic medications had a valid place, but that he always preferred other alternative methods. He once made a light-hearted comment which had its roots in the serious issue of overuse of medication:

'It would be much simpler if we could medicate the staff rather than the clients!'

This throwaway comment highlighted a view that we both shared; that there are always two or more people involved in a stressful situation, but, in the care world, it is the distressed or vulnerable person who receives the medication. It is true that people may need anti-depressant or anxiolytic medications to help them cope, at least in the short-term. Other medications, such as seizure preventatives, have a very clear purpose that benefits the physical health and well-being of an individual. It becomes more complicated when some of these same medications are used for other purposes such as behaviour control and mood stabilising, as is the case for certain anti-epileptic medications. In order to be confident managing distressed people without excessive use of medication, a change in mindset is required.

Control of the Environment

People who support individuals in community settings may sometimes feel isolated, especially if they are working alone (Rippon et al., 2019). This can create a sense of not being in control, and having little support. A sense of control will be reinforced if an environment contains safety measures, for example, toughened glass, isolation areas, monitoring and perimeter security. However, these measures may lead to a sense of overconfidence as well as of safety. An over-reliance on environmental measures can make us feel less able to control crisis situations on our own. Similarly, the use of alarms and sensors in secure facilities may empower the staff, but they may also create a loss of control for the people they support. There is a huge balancing act between supporting people to feel safe, and, at the same time, allowing individuals to have a high degree of perceived control. Sometimes people may feel more safe and secure by having colleagues with them. It has been my experience that this is 'a double-edged sword'. People may become overconfident if they have too much backup. It is also likely that an individual may have an increased risk of being restrained if there are too many staff present. In a series of classic studies in the 1980s, Albert Kushlick and his colleagues demonstrated that, in services for people with intellectual disabilities, higher staffing levels had a tendency to increase staff-to-staff rather than staff-to-client interaction. Similarly, people may feel more confident if they have some kind of personal alarm or warning system. Again, great care should be used with these systems. An alarm is only useful if it is guaranteed to attract help. The battle for control is a crucial issue for any low arousal practitioner.

Who is in Control?

There are several types of control to really focus on when applying non-confrontational approaches. Below are six ways in which issues of control can affect the way you interact with the people you support:

1) If you have a strong belief that a person has a high degree of control over their behaviour, this will increase your fear of them.

2) If you have a high degree of perceived control over your own behaviour, then you will be more confident when supporting people with distressed behaviour.

3) Seeing people as stressed and traumatised may help enable empathic understanding of how it may feel for them to have no control over their lives.

4) If you perceive someone to have a high degree of control over their behaviour, it can lead to more common usage of sanctions and restrictions.

5) A strong belief in the effectiveness of medication to control behaviour may lead to its overuse.

6) Environmental controls are important, but they may lead supporters to focus more on staff safety than positively supporting individuals.

Developing Self-Control

Perception of control has been a very strong theme in this chapter. How we develop self-control is a final key issue to consider. Most people may have an area of their life that they struggle to control. There are psychological studies which show that self-control in early childhood may lead to more positive aspects of self-control in adulthood. The psychologist Walter Mischel, in his book *The Marshmallow Test*, describes a whole series of studies which aim to help us understand how children develop self-control (2014). In these studies, children were offered a marshmallow, and told that they would be rewarded with another one if they could hold off on eating the first one until the tester returned in fifteen minutes time. Results showed that children who were able to delay gratification by waiting for the second marshmallow had better life outcomes in terms of educational success and physical health. Although these experiments are very interesting, the reader must be careful to avoid drawing over-simplistic conclusions. Self-control, like many other behaviours, tends to be context-driven. This means that a person may be able to develop a high sense of control in one situation, but not in another. If we consider the example of people with eating disorders, a person may be able to regulate their eating in certain social contexts and then binge, for example, when they are alone.

In the latter part of this book, we will discuss at great length the low arousal approach. Key to this philosophy is the idea that strategies which allow someone to develop more self-control are always going to be better than approaches which impose control upon an individual. This does not mean that we leave people to their own devices when they are highly distressed. We may try to assist people to make better decisions, for example by giving people advice about their physical health and well-being. The most important part of the Marshmallow Test studies is that if you can, for a short period of time, delay your reward or gratification, it will help you in your battle to achieve control.

Key Learning Questions

1) Why is perceived control an important need in our lives?

2) Why is it important to ensure that the people we support also have a high sense of perceived control?

3) What kind of problems can occur when we are overly-reliant on medication?

4) Think of a person you support who has strict rules and sanctions surrounding them. What would change if these rules were removed or altered so that the person had more control over their lives?

ACCEPTANCE, FORGIVENESS AND UNDERSTANDING

When we are involved with or support people who have a variety of challenging needs, it is very difficult to accept that those individuals may not want to change or alter their behaviour at that moment in time. Most people have an innate desire to help people, and this is a very important factor towards developing a society that cares. However, an overzealous approach to behaviour change goals can sometimes become an obstacle to support.

When supporting people who can be very distressed and challenging, it is important to be caring, safe and focused on the short-term, 'here and now' changes we can make to improve that person's well-being in the current moment. It can be hard to distinguish between our desire to change a person and the true reality of the situation, which is that change can take considerable time. Consider the parent who worries that their child is watching too much TV. They may make a firm decision to ban television, which will benefit the child in the long run as they may focus more on their education with less distraction. Most children, though they might complain, would generally accept this instruction over time. However, if the request is very likely to lead to an escalation in the child's behaviour, then this apparently simple goal may be a difficult thing to achieve. The parent making the request may become angry that the child has not accepted this rule, and the distress caused to both the child and the parent may potentially damage their relationship. Behaviour change is not easy, and parents in particular may find it extremely difficult to achieve. Acceptance that this process will take time and effort is necessary in order to bring about change.

Western Healthy Normality

The concept of acceptance has become an increasingly important part of therapeutic processes. We live in a society that can view the behaviours of others as being 'abnormal' or different. Western psychology is founded on the assumption of 'healthy normality' - that all humans are psychologically healthy, and should thrive in optimum conditions. In this case, behaviours that are unusual or unconventional are considered to be negative symptoms of abnormality. In essence, this assumption implies that people who do not fit the norm are damaged or broken and need to be repaired; that if we help people to 'fix' their problems then they will naturally be happy and content!

The concept of a healthy normality is, in my opinion, a very idealistic view of the world. Acceptance of a person does not mean that we should not intervene when they need help, but it does mean that we should question our motives for intervening. We should never assume that people can change, or even that they want to change. For practitioners of the low arousal approach, acceptance of both people and situations is necessary, which means having an almost opposite outlook than the assumption of healthy normality. There is no 'normal'. There are only people who can cope, and people who need help.

What Do We Mean By the Term Acceptance?

When we are supporting people who are highly distressed, we may well be exposed to a whole range of abusive behaviours. The concept of acceptance is a very useful one to consider in these situations. It may mean that we have to accept the complexity of a situation; namely, that we cannot easily control that person's behaviour. We may sometimes have to avoid personalising what the person has said to us, which often means accepting that they may be stressed or traumatised, and should therefore be treated with empathy. Often in these circumstances, we are left with unresolved feelings. We may behave in a very calm manner towards an individual during an incident, but afterwards experience a whole range of emotions including fear and anger. In these circumstances, we accept the situation, but not necessarily the feelings that follow. Resolving these inner conflicts is a very important part of any crisis management approach.

Acceptance and Commitment Therapy (ACT) is becoming a more popular tool to resolve workplace stress and other issues. The originator, Steven Hayes, designed the therapeutic approach by focusing less on getting rid of feelings, and more on staying 'in the moment' (Hayes et al., 1999). The ACT approach encourages healthy reconciliation with unpleasant feelings and situations. When applying a low arousal approach to behaviour management, accepting that we cannot always necessarily resolve our inner feelings can be quite liberating. Sometimes, people struggle to emotionally 'switch off' from hostile situations. The concept that supporters need to understand is that they cannot always alter or change the behaviour of a person who is being hostile.

Accepting What We Can Change

When are supporting people who are highly stressed, the best approaches often involve trying to deal with the 'here and now' rather than focusing on long-term goals. It is often the case that supporters can confuse managing behaviour with changing behaviours. When you are experiencing verbal aggression and threatening behaviours, the most important thing is to focus on the moment and what you can do to create a safe and calm situation. The following true example demonstrates how important this is:

'Jenny is a young mother with seven-year-old twin boys, both with a diagnosis of autism. Jenny receives some practical support to get them to school, but each day it is a struggle to get them to go onto their transport. Jenny knows that, most of the time, her children will settle down once they reach their classroom. The school has also reported difficulties when it comes to transporting the children back home. They refuse to enter the bus, and a lot of encouragement is needed. Again, once they are 'on the move' they appear to be fine.

Jenny was confused about how to manage her children's behaviour. She received conflicting advice from both families and professionals on a routine basis. The school staff advised her to give equal amounts of time to both children, to be 'firm' with them and to place some boundaries on the twins in order to help them to regulate their emotions. An educational psychologist who visited the home suggested that the children are 'developmentally young', and need time to develop both socially and emotionally. No advice was given about how to manage her children's behaviours when they became intense, or when the twins became aggressive towards each other. Her extended family is also split between two points of view. Some of them believe that she should be tougher and not give in to her children, whilst others maintain that giving in is not a sign of weakness, and may actually resolve the issue.

Jenny fluctuated between 'giving in' to the behaviours and becoming quite angry and distressed with her children. Much of the conflicting advice she had received did not make sense to her. Her approach began to change once she started to focus on her own behaviour instead of her children's. She began to concentrate on staying and appearing calm in the moments leading up to crisis incidents. In terms of getting the twins onto the bus, she slowed her responses down significantly, even forcing herself to move more slowly. The psychologist's advice that her children were developmentally quite young suggested to her that she needed to operate with fewer goals and worry less about the situation. In essence, she decided to accept that change is a difficult process, and therefore began to ignore over-simplistic advice.'

In the above example, Jenny began to realise that the issues she has with her children cannot be quickly altered. The psychologist's advice had an impact, and she began to interpret her children's behaviours in the short-term rather than focusing on too many behaviour change goals. Jenny managed to avoid taking 'quick fix',

Nanny 911 style advice that would not have benefitted her or her children. The simple analogy is that if your house is on fire, you should concentrate on the fire (the immediate concern) first, and worry about what happens afterwards at a later date.

Trying to problem solve and provide help is extremely difficult, especially if the person does not appear to want your help. Let us consider the following example:

'Tommy is a forty-five-year-old, unemployed man with long-term drug and alcohol addictions. He is currently living in a supervised domiciliary setting and is making his fourth attempt to 'get clean'. To remain in the programme, Tommy needs to commit to not drinking or using drugs. There have been occasions where staff have suspected that he has been drinking alcohol, which he always denies. In the past, Tommy has been known to fuel his habits by stealing from others. Tommy appears to really struggle with this process, and can often become extremely aggressive with some of the other people in the programme. He has threatened some of the staff in the programme with violence, especially if he is challenged about his compliance with the programme.'

This example shows how difficult it can be to accept that some people's struggles are not going to change very quickly. Depending on your point of view, Tommy can be seen as a 'victim' or as a 'bully'. It is often the case that people may view addictions as being 'self-inflicted', and that people should be prevented from making unhealthy and dangerous decisions. Alternatively, Tommy can be viewed as a deeply troubled person with a traumatised past, who cannot control his behaviour and is therefore unable to change. These differing views make a huge difference to how his behaviour is managed by others.

Good approaches to any form of behaviour management require a high level of tolerance. A low arousal approach is almost the opposite of 'zero tolerance' approaches, which encourage boundary-setting and assertiveness in the face of verbal or physical aggression. Instead, low arousal means tolerating behaviours that you may be inclined to want to change, and accepting that the first priority is often not the behaviour of concern itself, but the underlying causes such as stress and trauma.

'Riding Out the Storm' is Sometimes the Best Strategy

My colleague David Pitonyak often uses the analogy of riding out a storm on a ship to describe managing distressed behaviour. You cannot necessarily alter the weather or avoid the storm (although, of course, avoidance is a good strategy). There is no point in dwelling on things that you cannot change. In this example, the only option is to 'ride out' the storm by battening down the hatches and taking additional steps to make the ship as safe as possible. This analogy applies well to our work and the concept that we must focus on what can be achieved in the short-term. Riding out a storm can be a frightening but unavoidable experience. Similarly, situations that cannot be altered have to be managed rather than changed, and hopefully in future avoided.

Accepting a situation is just a natural part of any human process. The reality of this in terms of human behaviour is very clear, such that changing behaviours is a complicated and often long-term process. Even if the circumstances suggest a need to change behaviours, the reality is that, for real behaviour change to occur, a person has to be motivated to change as well as have the appropriate support available. In the modern world, we struggle to change everyday behaviours such as eating fast-food and smoking. It becomes even more challenging when we consider people with addictions. In a low arousal approach to crisis management, we do not simply give up on supporting people to change their behaviours. Instead, we try to focus on riding out the storm (aggression, violence, threats) until the ship reaches calmer waters, where the circumstances may be right to change course and avoid storms in the future.

When people struggle to accept that they must ride out the storm, it can often end up making situations much worse. Try to think of examples from your own life experience where someone was telling you that you needed to change a behaviour for your own good, and you became hostile or defensive. Pick a particular example that you remember well, and answer the following questions as honestly as you can:

1) How did you disagree with the person (did you argue, shut them down, storm off, become dismissive)?
2) Did you eventually take their advice?
3) If 'yes', what did you do to change the behaviour?
4) If 'no', what did you do instead?

Once you have completed this exercise, take some time to think about how you felt in that situation. It can be hard to be confronted with change, especially if we are not ready for it.

Forgiveness

How easy is it to forgive a person if they have offended, scared or harmed you? Forgiveness is sometimes a vital part of acceptance. The following contains a list of everyday behaviours that you may be faced with from friends, strangers or a close partner. Try to think about how easy it would be to forgive the person if they had done the following:

1- A friend lies to you about their behaviour.

2- A stranger lies to you about their behaviour.

3- A close partner lies to you about their behaviour.

4- A friend steals a small amount of cash from you.

5- A stranger steals a small amount of cash from you.

6- A close partner steals a small amount of cash from you.

7- A friend threatens to hurt you physically.

8- A stranger threatens to hurt you physically.

9- A close partner threatens to hurt you physically.

In the above examples, when would you be able to forgive the person? How much of a difference does it make whether you know the individual and how close they are to you?

There are many complicated processes involved in forgiveness. When we work with or support people who can be highly distressed, we are often exposed to verbal abuse, threats and, in some cases, intimidation. In more extreme circumstances, you may be physically hurt by a person, frightened or intimidated. It is not easy to forgive people in these circumstances.

When talking about acceptance and forgiveness, there are always going to be limits to what we can forgive in reality. The Irish hostage,

154

Brian Keenan, who was abducted and held hostage by fundamentalists in the Lebanon, wrote very honestly about this traumatic experience in his book *An Evil Cradling* (1992). Keenan wrote of his lack of forgiveness for the people who held and tortured him for four and a half years. For him, it was important that the deliberate torture and humiliation should not be forgiven, even though he felt he had managed to 'move on' from the experience.

If you think a person has directly tried to hurt you in a planned and premeditated manner, the process of acceptance and forgiveness can be a difficult one. However, we can sometimes be surprisingly forgiving if we do not personalise the behaviour in relation to ourselves. The following example sets a major gold standard for any person working in care when it comes to forgiveness:

'Imogen works in a supported living setting. The person she supports, Frank, has an acquired brain injury and a childhood history of abuse. He has been described by many people who know him as being an extremely angry person. Imogen has developed a very good working relationship with him and, although he often becomes angry with her colleagues, it is a rarity for him to express negative feelings openly towards her. One afternoon, Frank was very upset and began to accuse people of stealing his things from his bedroom. Imogen knew that it was unlikely anything had been stolen, but she was very concerned that he might run off and sleep rough, which he done in the past. He had also drank heavily in these situations before.

Frank told Imogen that he was leaving, and she instinctively stood in his way at the top of the stairs in his house. He tried to push her out of the way, and Imogen fell backwards, injuring her back (she was off work for nearly a month). Frank ran off in panic. A few days later, he wrote Imogen a letter saying that he was sorry and he had not meant to hurt her. Despite being physically and emotionally shaken, Imogen returned to work and insisted that she worked with Frank. She told her shocked colleagues, "How can I blame him? I shouldn't have blocked his way, and I know he did not mean to hurt me".'

In the above scenario, Imogen sets an incredibly high standard for people to follow. Despite being physically hurt, she learned to accept the situation as an accident, and was then able to forgive the individual. Her already established connection with Frank and her understanding of his distressed behaviour aided her ability to forgive.

Explaining and Understanding Behaviours

Accepting that behaviour cannot rapidly change and learning to forgive when you have been harmed requires some sort of framework for understanding why a person behaves in the way that they do. If a person is abusive or aggressive towards us, it does seem to be easier if we have some understanding of why they are behaving in that way. The following real-life example demonstrates the power that an explanation has to calm a situation:

'Laurence was working in his garden (an activity that he did not particularly enjoy). His three young children were being quite noisy, playing in their paddling pool. The family had not met their new neighbours at the time - but they were about to. Laurence heard a female voice scream, "Shut those children up!" The abusive language was highly personal and upsetting to all members of the family.

Laurence was extremely angry and upset, and immediately ran to the neighbour's house. However, after ringing the neighbour's doorbell, he was confronted with an elderly man who looked visibly scared and upset. The man apologised, saying, "My wife has just gotten out of hospital and she is not feeling that great". Immediately, Laurence felt ashamed of reacting in such an aggressive manner. He made sure that his children played in the house for the rest of the weekend.'

There is a considerable body of psychological research which demonstrates that when we cannot explain a behaviour, we may start to view the person in a negative manner. We have a tendency to not want to help people whom we perceive to be in control of their behaviour. Understanding these automatic judgements and becoming more self-aware is an important step in the process of reflection, as our own beliefs and biases can impact our ability to empathise and understand.

In summary, acceptance, forgiveness and understanding are three very important parts of relationship building. When working with vulnerable people, we often need to be able to respond in a low-key or minimalist manner. To do this requires us to accept the person as they are, and also that we cannot always have solutions to difficult problems. It most certainly requires some form of understanding of that individual, which requires us to be reflective and empathic practitioners. Finally, it is inevitable that you will be exposed to verbal and sometimes even physical abuse from distressed individuals. In these instances, it is more important than ever to view the individual as stressed and traumatised, and to accept that they are not fully in control of their behaviour.

Key Learning Questions

1) What do we understand by the term 'acceptance'?

2) What is the difference between managing and changing a behaviour?

3) How do we resolve negative emotions from the people we support?

4) How easy is it to forgive someone who has hurt you? Think of a personal instance where you have struggled to forgive.

PART TWO: MANAGING DISTRESSING SITUATIONS

CHAPTER 9

UNDERSTANDING PHYSIOLOGICAL AROUSAL

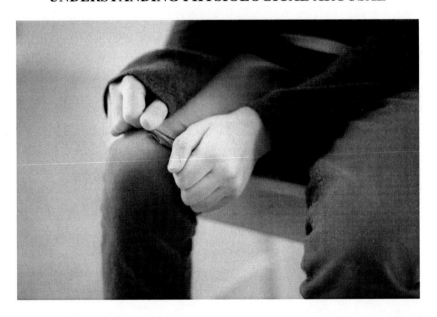

Arousal is part of our survival mechanism. Many of us are aware of the need for regulated and balanced physiological systems. Arousal involves a complex number of brain and bodily processes, and there are many different arousal mechanisms in the body. Understanding these mechanisms can help us to better respond to people in crisis situations, who will often be experiencing high levels of arousal.

There are obviously situations in which a heightened state of arousal can have a positive function. Increased arousal makes us more alert and, in some circumstances, more focused. A good everyday example is people who are highly skilled at complex motor tasks. A tightrope walker needs to be in balance and harmony, both mentally and physically; if that person became hyper aroused then they would lose their balance. Similarly, if their arousal level was too low, they might not be sufficiently focused and aware of the needs of their task.

The best way to think about these arousal systems is to think of a car engine. A car may have an idling speed that just about keeps it moving. If you need to get somewhere fast, you can move up through the gears and work the engine hard. With cars as with humans, the basic level of arousal varies depending on the situation.

An example of a low state of arousal is sleep. Our heart rate drops when we are asleep, allowing it to simply 'tick over' and keep our basic bodily functions working. When we become increasingly aroused, our brain sends signals to our body that increase our alertness. This does not always have to be a threat warning. We might become attracted to someone in a room, smell a particularly pleasant food or become excited by good news. Being aware of these internal bodily reactions and what they mean helps us to make sense of the world. Sometimes, not understanding these reactions can lead to real problems for people.

Let us think about what happens when our arousal level increases in a rapid manner. We often talk about the fight or flight mechanism. When we are in a heightened state of arousal, we will either confront the thing that threatens us, or run away from it. In terms of crisis management, running away, or avoidance, can actually be a very appropriate strategy at times. I have learned from personal experience that sometimes people need to be provided with an escape route in certain situations, especially if they feel trapped or as though there is no way out. Similarly, you can be involved in a crisis situation where not confronting someone who is in a state of hyperarousal is the most sensible reaction. This is due to the fact that a person in a state of hyperarousal may be processing information more slowly than usual, and is therefore more likely to perceive someone as threatening when there is no hostile intent. There is also a third option, whereby people will simply freeze. In the Second World War, submariners would often hide to avoid detection. Interestingly, American submarine captains were notoriously aggressive when attacking ships, but they were also wisely taught to avoid engaging when they had a very small chance of success.

Arousal and Emotion

Arousal mechanisms are very basic, and affect us in terms of our thinking processes and decision making. Try to think about arousal mechanisms as being part of the warning system in terms of your own experiences. Consider the following situations, rating them from 1-5:

> 1 - not too arousing, 2 - slightly arousing, 3 - moderately arousing, 4 - strongly arousing, 5 - very arousing

1) A stranger shouts at you

2) A person runs towards you quickly

3) A car back-fires

4) Being on a rollercoaster ride

5) Taking off or landing in an airplane

6) A sudden thunder clap

7) Insects flying around you

8) Being touched by others without warning

9) Being in a waiting room for an interview for a job

10) Being in a completely dark and strange place

11) The sight of human blood

12) Swimming in deep water

13) Being in a very crowded room

14) Being around barking dogs

15) Being asked to speak in public to a group of strangers

16) Meeting and hugging an old friend

17) Being physically attracted to another person

18) Eating an extremely hot chilli pepper

19) Smelling something fragrant and nice

20) Tasting something incredible

What Does This Tell Us About Arousal?

Hopefully these questions have made you aware of how your own arousal levels are affected by the environment. In this list, there are some examples which are universally arousing, and impossible not to respond to on an instinctual level. Others vary in their arousal responses to certain things. For example, for many people, flying on a plane is simply not a problem, but for others it is a terrifying experience. There are some situations that depend more on our personal life experiences, and others that demonstrate how even pleasant stimuli can trigger arousal.

Looking at warning mechanisms and their common responses (fight, flight or freeze), it is clear that increases in arousal not only vary, but they also influence how we behave. Arousal is so important to understand when it comes to behaviour, and that is why this manual focuses on how to manage arousal and the behaviour that results from it. We will now look at situations where arousal increases, either because we feel threatened or excited. Awareness of our bodily responses is a critical part of being connected to the world. Concepts such as Mindfulness require people to focus on the here-and-now, tuning in to their bodily states and the world around them. A prominent psychologist at the end of the nineteenth century, William James, was one of the first people to suggest that we label our bodily sensations (1884). In the hundred years since, the idea that people's thoughts and cognitions can evoke a bodily response has become more popular. In fact, this concept is the cornerstone of cognitive behavioural therapy (CBT). I will admit to being much more 'Jamesian' in my approach in the sense that it is my view that people who sometimes struggle to understand their internal bodily world and connect it to the external world would benefit immensely from giving a name to their bodily sensations. Take the following for example:

'Astrid is a teenage girl living in a specialist facility due to her diagnosis of an eating disorder. Astrid has to be monitored when she eats to make sure that she obtains the minimum calories required to

survive. Astrid struggles to make sense of her body's reactions, and often states that she feels full after relatively small quantities of food have been consumed.'

Whilst Astrid's example is highly complex and interconnected with her fear of eating, her heighted state of arousal when eating leads to physical symptoms of panic, whereby the brain bypasses the stomach as it is not essential for a survival response. This means that her ability to make sense of her internal bodily state has become faulty, and she does not understand that the reason she feels full is because she is scared. There are many complex reasons behind her eating disorder, but sometimes, for people like Astrid, understanding and being able to identify the basic mechanisms of the body can help them to make sense of the world.

Our brains are constantly striving to make sense of the world around us. We often experience things internally which we then try to label afterwards. It has long been known that our arousal mechanism has an immense impact on how we process information. We know that novel, unpredictable things can lead to an increased arousal response. The link between arousal and information processing was originally described by two American researchers, Robert Yerkes and John Dodson (1908). We now know this as the 'Yerkes-Dodson Law', which maintains that performance and arousal are linked in a classic inverted U shape, and proposes that high levels of arousal consequently decrease human performance.

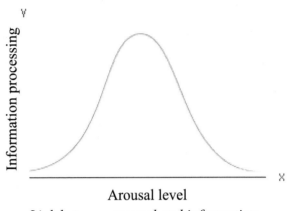

Arousal level

Link between arousal and information

Conversely, the law also demonstrates that moderate levels of arousal can increase the brain's processing ability, implying an optimum level of arousal for human performance. Both under and over arousal (the two extremes of the curve) will lead to poor performance in any task. The goal for anyone learning new information or skills is to achieve a state of balance. The correct term for this is 'arousal homeostasis' (McDonnell et al., 2014).

Stress and Arousal

The term stress was first used extensively by a Hungarian endocrinologist named Hans Selye (1956). Selye's early research introduced the idea that the body experiences stress as a natural reaction, and argued that the experience of stress was not always negative for an individual (1976). Stress is a concept that is often used interchangeably with the word anxiety. Personally, I prefer the word stress as it tends to focus more on the link between people and their environment. Anxiety, on the other hand, refers to a person's internal interpretation of that environment. For example, we can refer to a person as being anxious or suffering from OCD, whereas the term stress is broader and encapsulates both of these discrete areas. One of the classic models of psychological stress was proposed in the 1980's by Richard Lazarus and Susan Folkman, elements of which appear in many other models of psychological stress (1984). This transactional model of stress emphasises the interaction between an individual and their environment. Stress occurs when the demands of the stressors outweigh the abilities of the coping responses. Implicit in this model is the cognitive appraisal of threat, whereby there is a clear interaction between environmental and physiological events. When it comes to behaviours of concern such as aggression and self-injury, it is thought that these physiologically arousing behaviours are actually a means of relieving stress (Groden et al., 1994). If this model suggests that there is a transaction between a person's internal state of arousal and environmental stressors, then the reduction of environmental triggers should decrease stress, and thus reduce the frequency and intensity of behaviours of concern.

There is a very clear link between stress and arousal. To understand the interaction between these concepts, it is best to think of them as two sides of a coin. Arousal mechanisms are part of our day-to-day processes. The autonomic nervous system can be divided into two parts: the sympathetic and parasympathetic. The sympathetic nervous system focuses on the basic processes that affect the fight or flight responses. The parasympathetic nervous system is responsible for slowing the body down - this usually occurs when the body is at rest or after eating. The sympathetic and parasympathic nervous systems interact to create a sense of balance in the body, linked to our brain via neurotransmitters. In the same way that stress triggers the sympathetic nervous system, high levels of arousal also trigger the same responses.

We are only just beginning to fully understand the complexities of different types of stress responses in the body. To give a good example of how the fight or flight response can lead to long-term stress, let us consider the survival response from a different perspective. If we are in a threatening situation, our arousal mechanism will react. Initially, we will experience an increase in adrenaline and a spike in heart rate. If this is in response to something that is a 'one-off event' (such as a car backfiring), then the body will soon return to a state of balance or homeostasis. However, if the threat is persistent, such as someone being verbally threatening and aggressive towards you, then the body maintains a high level of alertness. Biologically, the body achieves this by secreting the hormone cortisol. Cortisol has many functions, but in these circumstances, it sustains alertness after the initial adrenaline surge. Simply, heightened levels of cortisol allow your body to be highly reactive for prolonged periods of time.

My colleagues at the University of Northumbria have been working with Studio3 to examine stress responses in the context of carers (Rippon et al., 2019). In a very recent study, they found that carers who supported people with dementia had abnormally high cortisol levels compared to students and university lecturers. These recent studies suggest that the link between psychological and biological stress is still poorly understood.

Arousal and Behaviours of Concern

Stress and anxiety have been proposed as factors which affect the frequency of behaviours of concern in people with autism spectrum disorder (ASD), and in everyday work situations (Howlin, 1998; Chen and Spector, 1992). An understanding of the stress response is therefore useful in the development of effective behaviour management strategies. Linsley (2006) recognised that arousal itself does not inherently entail violence, but that there is a strong link between high levels of arousal and aggression.

Understanding the role of arousal levels in incidents of aggression and violence allows carers to manage these situations by working to lower arousal levels. Whilst heightened arousal does not necessarily cause aggression, aggressive incidents rarely occur when an individual is in a low state of arousal. How aroused a person is influences the way they interpret and react to environmental stimuli. A stress-free individual in a calm environment is less likely to engage in behaviours of concern as a means of relieving stress.

Individuals naturally seek a state of *arousal equilibrium*, i.e. the optimum level of arousal required for them to function in an environment. The majority of individuals spend most of their time in this state. In the case of individuals with behaviours of concern, two distinct arousal groupings have a pronounced effect on their behaviour. Both states of arousal appear in the tail-end of the arousal curve; under and over arousal. Individuals who are hyper aroused (over aroused) are highly reactive to environmental sensory stimuli, and are therefore powerfully influenced by 'hot' processes (Anderson and Bushman, 2002). A 'hot' process means that the person is reacting almost without thinking. The opposite of this involves 'cool' processes, whereby a person is logical and methodical in their thinking. In other situations, people who are hypo aroused (under aroused) may fail to react to environmental stimuli, thus resulting in a breakdown of communication and social isolation.

The application of arousal to behaviours of concern should be first thought of in terms of the person who is experiencing a particular threat or challenge. We know that individual carers will often be exposed to many forms of behaviour which will increase their stress and arousal levels. As we have already seen, people often struggle to cope with the biological consequences of being stressed. Their cortisol and adrenaline levels may reach a point where they are unable to process what the other person is saying or doing. In these circumstances, the psychologist Susanna Miller points to the phenomenon of 'monitoring' and 'blunting' (Miller, 1995). These are coping strategies which people often use to adjust to stressful life events. Monitors are usually people who are highly attentive and sensitive, who tend to amplify perceived threats. Conversely, blunters are less attentive and see things as being less urgent. Blunters may underestimate risks, whereas monitors may overestimate risk: in extreme situations, neither type of person functions very well. The following example was described to me by a researcher who studied air accidents and near-misses:

'There is a point midway across the Pacific Ocean where there are no airfields to land upon for 1000 miles or so. In modern aviation, pilots can become a little nervous flying over airspace, where there is no place to divert to in the event of an emergency. It is alleged that on one particular flight, an airliner developed a problem involving accidental fuel loss, which meant that the plane might not be safely able to reach an airport. Airline crews are taught to be calm, and to provide information and reassurance to passengers in circumstances such as these. Due to some excellent flying and engineering skills, the captain realised that they would in fact be able to divert and land safely. Following procedure, he informed the passengers of the good news. There was nearly a riot on the plane. It appears that the chief Stewardess, instead of following the procedure of calmness and reassurance, had instead proceeded to give out free alcohol to people on the flight and refrain from telling them that there was a problem. When this matter was investigated however, she was indeed able to describe the emergency procedure in full, down to the very smallest detail.'

This example illustrates how, when in a state of heighted arousal and stress, a person may not react in the way we expect, or the way they have been trained. It could be argued that the Stewardess may have become hyper aroused due to the nature of the emergency, and could therefore not focus on procedure. It is likely that in this moment she became a 'blunter' and could not face the issue at hand. The interesting question is: can people learn from these situations?

Would it be true that in another similar situation, this person would react in exactly the same way again?

The effects of hyperarousal can also influence our work as care givers, whereby highly stressful crisis situations can similarly cause us to forget our training and panic. So how can we learn to stop, breathe and think in these threatening situations? Lowering our own arousal levels means that we are better equipped to deal with critical situations, and can logically and rationally approach the problem without panicking. A low arousal approach to managing behaviours of concern requires people to be relatively calm in threatening situations. Carers need to be able to manage their own stress so that they are able to approach situations in a confident, almost 'twilight state' of mind. There is a great deal of research which indicates that stress management strategies can help an individual to control their physiological experience of stress and arousal. The four most common strategies include: Mindfulness and other relaxation methods, cardiac exercise, achieving a 'flow state', and a strong focus on physical well-being.

Mindfulness and Relaxation

There is some debate about the various forms of relaxation methods and Mindfulness-based techniques. All methods share a common goal; to achieve a state, both physiologically and mentally, of positive equilibrium or balance. There are convincing arguments for a variety of methods, many of which have origins in Eastern Buddhist philosophy. Ryan Niemiec identifies two simple processes involved in what he refers to as 'The Mindful Pause' (2016). The first is to breathe for 10-15 seconds, letting go of any stress and tension you are feeling. The second involves grounding yourself in the present moment by asking what you can bring to the current situation in order to resolve or better it. This requires tuning in to the 'here-and-now' when we might otherwise become preoccupied with things that will happen in the future. The Mindful Pause is a useful tool for low arousal practitioners who find themselves in stressful situations. Mindfulness has been further defined by some as a means of self-regulating our own attention, which is achieved through adopting an attitude of openness, curiosity and acceptance. Quite simply, Mindfulness is essentially a method of slowing our thought processes down as a means of reducing stress.

There are also a number of studies which show that training in Mindfulness may actually have a positive impact on levels of psychological stress, and reduce the frequency of behaviours of concern (Shonin et al., 2015). If there is a word of caution to be said, it is that Mindfulness-based methods vary in their suitability depending on the individual. The Benson Method uses a much more behaviour-based approach which involves the individual chanting a word or phrase to themselves whilst concentrating on their breathing (Benson, 2000). This relaxation method achieves a state of 'tuning out' and is similar to forms of 'thought blocking' (McCreadie and McDermott, 2014).

Cardiac Exercise

Cardiac exercise has a huge impact on stress and well-being. If we were to apply stress management skills from an evidence-based perspective, then every practitioner reading this book would be encouraged to routinely engage in some form of regular cardiac exercise. There are many studies which demonstrate that regular cardiac exercise is positive for our physical health, being associated with a lower risk of heart failure and increased well-being. Aerobic exercise can also have a positive impact on cognitive functioning for children in classrooms (Bidzan-Bluma and Lipowska, 2018).

Cardiac exercise can produce positive physiological changes in relatively short periods of time, such as reducing levels of the stress hormone cortisol (Alghdier, Gabr and Aly, 2015). There is therefore little doubt that regular cardiac exercise would have a positive impact on individuals who are hyper aroused or highly distressed. It has already been stated that consistently high levels of cortisol can have a negative effect on people's ability to function. I have found that cardiac exercise is crucial to helping individuals regulate their own arousal mechanisms. Personally, I would suggest that adults should do a minimum of 2 hours and 30 minutes a week of moderate exercise, and at least 1 hour and 30 minutes a week of intensive exercise. The effects of regular exercise on stress are widely recorded, therefore exercise should be viewed as primary intervention for anyone who is distressed or who works in a highly stressful environment. It is commonly said that if exercise could be turned into a pill, it would be the most powerful drug that doctors could prescribe. Personally, I have found that cardiac exercise is a crucial factor in helping individuals to regulate their own arousal mechanisms.

If exercise is so powerful, why is it not a more central part of everyone's weekly regime? The simple answer is that exercise is difficult and requires major lifestyle changes, and quite often people who are highly stressed cannot or do not make the time. Another difficulty is that, apart from the 'endorphin highs' that people can experience, the effects of exercise take a considerable length of time to have a noticeable, positive impact. My view is that there has been too much emphasis over the years on the use of cardiac exercise for weight loss. Studies show that the effects of cardiac exercise alone are insufficient to achieve significant weight loss in most people. Furthermore, the message that this societal emphasis on weight loss conveys is the wrong one. Cardiac exercise should be used, but primarily to reduce physiological stress.

Flow States

Psychologist Mihayli Czikszentmihalyi described a flow state as a situation where someone 'is in the zone' - so absorbed in an activity that they tune out of the world around them (1990). Typical activities where flow states can be achieved are reading, playing games such as chess, running, knitting or drawing. It is important to note that flow does not require higher order activities in order to be achieved. Any activity or task where a person can be totally absorbed should count as a flow activity. Consider the following example:

'Rory is a fourteen-year-old boy with a diagnosis of autism and ADHD. Rory really struggles to focus for prolonged periods of time in day-to-day classroom settings. The only exception to this appears to be when he is given a quantity of lego to play with. He becomes so absorbed in the activity that his teachers describe him as being much calmer.'

In Rory's case, the flow state is achieved by an engaging task. Similarly, any hobby or interest that is absorbing to this degree would also count as a flow activity. Often, people who reject more traditional forms of Mindfulness or exercise-based interventions can achieve a sense of flow through a simple everyday task; even playing computer games, cleaning, and driving can help some people to achieve a flow state. The key is to switch off from the outside worries and problems, and focus solely on the physical task in front of you.

Physical Well-being

Achieving a state of balance and overall well-being requires a whole range of areas. The psychologist, Martin Seligman, argues that five main factors are essential for well-being (2011):

- Positive emotion (such as happiness)

- Engagement (in activities of interest)

- Relationships (with other people)

- Meaning (in our lives)

- Achievement/Accomplishment (of goals)

Whilst there can be no doubt that these are incredibly important elements, one of the building blocks for well-being is also physical well-being. Long-term stress can have strong negative effects on your physical health. The mechanisms involved in stress reactions also implicate our immune systems. To give an example, people who are chronically stressed are far more likely to develop minor complaints such as colds, ear infections and gastric problems (Takkouche, 2001). If you are working in a highly stressful situation, your physical health - including diet, hydration, and quality of sleep - become far more important.

The following exercise is designed to help the reader think about their own stress management strategies. Try to answer the following questions as honestly as possible.

THE REFLECTIVE JOURNEY

Do you engage at least weekly with any of the following:

1. Light cardiac activity (e.g. 2-3 hours of walking per week).
   YES/NO
2. Intensive cardiac exercise (e.g. 1-2 hours running a week).
   YES/NO
3. Do you participate in a physical sport or are you a member of a sports club?
   YES/NO
4. Do you practice for 10-15 minutes per day some form of Mindfulness or meditation?
   YES/NO
5. Do you drink more than 2 litres of fluid per day?
   YES/NO
6. Do you have any absorbing hobbies or interests?
   YES/NO
7. Do you regularly eat 3 meals per day?
   YES/NO
8. Do you suffer from gastric complaints, headaches or other health problems on a regular basis?
   YES/NO

These questions are deliberately phrased to look at your coping strategies for stress. Do not worry - most people, when they reflect on this, score pretty badly. The stress management skills we have described can apply to the people we support, but most importantly they apply to ourselves. As we have already discussed, stress is transactional in nature, and so the first step towards reducing stress in an individual's environment is reducing the stress that we may carry into their space.

In this book, have begun to focus on day-to-day crisis management, which includes many stressful situations. There needs to be a 'mindset change' in order to become a low arousal practitioner. When you completed the simple questions above, how many of you thought, 'I don't have the time to do all of these things'? When you prioritise self-care, the impact on your physical and emotional well-being, and of course your stress, will make you more resilient in the face of adversity. In my opinion, people need to be more focused on their stress management in general. The key to stress reduction is not monitoring how stressed you are, but focusing on how effective your coping strategies are. The next part of this book will focus in detail on the Low Arousal Approach to managing crises. It is not so much about preventing behaviours of concern and crisis situations from occurring, but more about staying in the moment and focusing on what you can do to bring about rapid reductions in physiological arousal. Applying a stress management approach by regulating your own arousal will also help you to regulate the arousal of others.

Key Learning Questions

1) What do we mean when we say a person is 'highly aroused'? How does this affect them on a physiological level?

2) How are stress and arousal linked?

3) Name three ways to reduce stress and arousal.

4) Think about how to implement these stress reduction strategies in your own life. For example, what activities do you enjoy that put you in a 'flow state'?

CHAPTER 10

THE LOW AROUSAL APPROACH

Managing behaviours of concern involves prevention, de-escalation and, in extreme cases, physical management. There are many times when people find themselves in situations in which they simply cannot prevent an incident from occurring. Originally, I developed this approach because there was little information that could be used to apply a scientific model to crisis management. This chapter will describe the development and evolution of a de-escalation model, which is now widely known as the Low Arousal Approach (McDonnell, Waters and Jones, 2002). This approach has evolved to become a practical behaviour management guide, not only for people with intellectual disabilities and autism, but for the care sector in general (McDonnell, 2010). To develop any de-escalation approach in care environments, a number of key issues require careful examination.

Philosophy of the Approach

The low arousal approach is a person-centred, non-confrontational method of managing behaviour. A key part of the approach is adopting a humanistic view of people. There are many different roots of humanism. The philosophical origins of the approach reflects other humanistic approaches that focus on non-violence, such as Buddhism. There is also a rich history of restraint reduction and humanism promoted by various Quaker organisations. In the UK, the York Retreat became famous for its 'no restraint' approach to supporting people with mental health issues. Similarly, a town called Gheel in Belgium developed an international reputation for applying community-based approaches to people with a range of conditions. If there is one essential component to these various approaches, it is basic human kindness and what is best described as 'tender loving care'.

An excellent example of a low arousal approach from long before the term was officially coined is the work of Jean-Marc-Gaspard Itard with a young man named Victor, more commonly referred to as 'The Wild Boy of Aveyron' (1802). Victor was a boy who was reported to be living ferally in France. In 1800, aged approximately twelve, he emerged naked from the forest. Itard, only a young medical student at the time, made many attempts to educate Victor with some degree of success. He was, however, unable to improve Victor's use of spoken language, which he considered to be a failure on his part. The humanity of his approach towards Victor is very clear in his writings. They developed a close relationship well beyond the bounds of a doctor and his patient. Whilst the idea of 'feral children' is still a controversial topic, the philosophy underpinning Itard's humanistic approach could be seen as very similar to what we now describe as 'low arousal'.

Another underlying theme of the low arousal approach is the avoidance of using punishment in response to behaviours of concern. An early advocate of this approach was the Polish educator Janus Korczak. Korczak was involved with supporting children in Orphanages in Warsaw during the Second World War. Korczak was very much a man ahead of his time with regards to the rights of children, long before the United Nations was formed. In his book *The Child's Right to Respect* (1929), he was very outspoken against corporal punishment at a time when such treatment was considered a parental entitlement, or even duty. One of his arguments cited not just cruelty, but the sense of powerlessness that smacking or hitting children creates. Korczak believed very strongly that parents should not use forms of physical punishment on children. His argument still applies today; that is, that children (and adults) should be treated with dignity and respect. Tragically, Korczak died a victim of the Holocaust in 1942 alongside the children who lived in the Orphanage.

A Brief History of the Development of the Guiding Principles

The growth of behavioural psychology, particularly in the latter part of the twentieth century, created a multitude of moral dilemmas for practitioners. The use of aversive consequences, such as forms of punishment, became a very controversial subject. Some practices involved extremely controversial approaches, for example the use of electric shocks to manage a range of behaviours, from self-injury to physical aggression. Physical punishments in Western Society are now less of an issue, but debates about the 'ends justifying the means' are part of our moral compass. These extreme arguments do not necessarily help people to understand that abuse of power is a huge part of the problem. The reality is that these arguments tend to overshadow day-to-day issues that are prevalent in many care facilities, such as the use of sanctions or withdrawal of privileges, which people justify far too easily. Consider the following example:

'Sally is a thirty-year-old woman with autism who lives in a group home with four other people. Sometimes she will become very argumentative with the other people she lives with. These arguments can become quite intense. Her support staff, who have received training in behaviour supports, have introduced a reward system to regulate her behaviour. Sally earns points for the days that she shows appropriate behaviour, and these points can then be converted into rewards of her choice. For example, she loves one-to-one time with staff and going to the shops. The programme has been regarded as successful, with a 50% reduction in behavioural incidents in the house. Nonetheless, she still has 'bad days' occasionally.'

What are the problems with this approach? This example has been chosen to show a seemingly harmless day-to-day practice that reflects a problem of power rather than effectiveness. Sally is highly motivated to have quality time with staff, to the point where she fears losing control and not earning her rewards. There are days where she struggles to regulate her own behaviour. These days she does not earn her rewards, which has a huge impact on her emotional well-being. In this example, Sally is in position of hopelessness due to being externally controlled by other people. There is little doubt that success can be achieved to a certain degree by using external regulation, but the goal should be to help people to regulate their own behaviour, not to attempt to control it through external measures.

History of the Low Arousal Approach

The low arousal approach was developed for a number of reasons. Firstly, it was a response to observing people in community and institutional settings who were often exposed to punitive practices by their carers. It is not unusual for distressed people to be overwhelmed by boundaries and rules, and we see this so often in our work. Secondly, it was obvious that the behaviour of staff and carers appeared to directly trigger behaviours of concern in distressed individuals. Carers often behaved in a manner that characterised individuals as either 'victims' or 'perpetrators'. Thirdly, in many cases, physical restraint appeared to be used in an unplanned and unsafe manner. It was also often the first rather than 'the last resort' in many care settings. Physical restraint methods are coercive in nature, and in some extreme situations, can lead to tragedies and fatalities. The simple concept of the low arousal approach was to make people focus more on safe and effective de-escalation techniques, and less on confrontation. The approach is still evolving and now has many international contributors. It has been successfully applied in a range of services and areas, including intellectual disabilities, older adults, as well as children and adult mental health services.

1986-1990: Development of Early Crisis Management Training

Training courses in crisis management, to this present day, tend to have quite mixed messages. We often train people to de-escalate situations, but then also teach them how to physically restrain people. Training in the mid-1980s in the UK was quite a variable menu.

Personally, I attended a number of training courses with titles along the lines of 'Managing Violence' etc, where the underlying theme was one of no clear rationale for de-escalating incidents. The physical skills taught were often taken from a variety of martial arts, with training held in gymnasiums and even sports facilities. The most established system in the UK at that time was called 'Control and Restraint', an approach which appeared to originate in the UK Prison Service. I found myself unnerved by the fact that the type of challenges I faced working with individuals who had intellectual disabilities were not the same as the kind of violence that inmates could engage in. This level of violence, however, is what most training courses seemed to be geared towards.

In 1987, I ran a two-day pilot training course at Monyhull Hospital for people with disabilities in Birmingham, UK. The core aim was to avoid teaching any kind of physical restraint that involved taking people to the floor. Nearly two thirds of the programme contained physical methods as this was what frontline staff mostly requested. The term 'low arousal' was not used at the time; expressions such as 'non-confrontation' and 'non-violent responding' were more commonly used. This was the early origin of the Studio3 programme.

Between 1990-2000, core training lasting three days in duration was developed, which was approximately 50% dedicated to managing physical situations. Subsequently, in 1992, the organisation Studio3 was formed. The term 'Low Arousal Approach' began to be used in the early 1990's, having evolved from a strong humanist philosophy (McDonnell, McEvoy and Dearden, 1994). The fundamental idea was that arousal was something that was shared in situations, and that reducing arousal, mostly by environmental changes, was a key tool when managing crisis situations. In a case study published on an adult with intellectual disabilities and behaviours of concern, the early definition of low arousal focused strongly on the behaviour of staff and carers. This study defined low arousal approaches as 'attempts to alter staff behaviour by avoiding confrontational situations and seeking the least line of resistance' (McDonnell, Reeves, Johnson and Lane, 1998: p.164).

My colleagues and I also published a series of studies examining specific forms of physical restraint (McDonnell, 2010). The social validity of physical interventions became a strong theme in my work. The simple way to think about sociability would be to judge how a procedure or intervention would look if it was demonstrated in front of many witnesses who had little or no experience of physical restraint. It is often helpful to think about a way to discuss these issues by imagining that you had to physically restrain someone in a supermarket, with members of the public watching. The acid test of a restraint method's humanity would be whether bystanders would immediately call the police, or judge the procedure to be humane. This became a cornerstone of developing socially valid methods within Studio3. The idea was extended across all contexts, namely that any form of restraint should be designed to be effective, safe, and socially valid. I have always found it important that we try to get people to understand, from an empathic point of view, what it is like for a child or adult to be restrained. Staff on Studio3 training courses were often expected to themselves experience many aversive restraint holds, and thus actively encouraged to empathise with the people they supported.

The definition of the low arousal approach evolved to include a stronger focus on reflective practice, with four key elements to managing crisis situations:

1) Decreasing demands and requests to reduce potential points of conflict around an individual.

2) Avoidance of potentially arousing triggers, e.g. direct eye contact, touch, and removal of spectators to the incident.

3) Avoidance of non-verbal behaviours that may lead to conflict, e.g. aggressive postures and stances.

4) Challenging carer beliefs about the short-term management of behaviours of concern.

Gradually increasing from the year 2000 to the present, Studio3 now runs training courses in fourteen different countries across the globe, with a focus on applying low arousal approaches in behaviour management. The concept has been reformulated to include cognitive aspects (McDonnell, Waters and Jones, 2002). In addition, it has been applied to supporting family members to manage crises (Woodcock and Page, 2010).

Violence is Situation-Specific and Training Should Reflect This

Over the last 25 years, there has been a strong debate in the crisis management industry about the nature of the violence that people encounter in care situations. In the news, we read reports of serious crime. The psychologist Stanley Rachman, in his book *Fear and Courage* (1978), argued that fear can be transmitted through the simple communication of information. Training programmes which focus on managing violence often portray the most extreme forms of aggressive behaviour, which are a rarity in care environments. On a training programme many years ago, I was once asked what technique I would use to defend myself against multiple attackers. The answer was simple: "I would run". My response to the questioner was, "How likely is that to happen?"

I was also once asked why Studio3 trainers do not address serious attacks with weapons such as knives. Whilst it is true that knife crime is a frightening thing, in most societies it is a relatively rare phenomenon. Having been an instructor in the martial art of Jiu Jitsu for nearly 30 years, achieving a high skill level involving thousands of hours of training, if a knife-wielding attacker ran towards me, I would still run. It is simply not possible to train people on brief training courses to defend themselves against such extreme and rare attacks. It is important that people understand why we only train staff to manage everyday, common situations and not extreme ones.

To illustrate this point, some of the most honest feedback ever given on a Studio3 training programme came from a manager who had spent twenty years in the UK military, including the Special Forces:

THE REFLECTIVE JOURNEY

"When I was a soldier, I could rely on military firepower for all the support I needed. Now I work in a care home for adults with intellectual disabilities without any military arsenal. I love this work, and I cannot understand why people view the violence we encounter in care settings at the same level as other, life-threatening situations. People need to understand that I can still be scared in care situations, but that my responses need to be totally different."

Preparing for extreme situations makes for bad training courses. It is important to avoid generating ridiculous 'what if' scenarios, especially while the crisis management training industry is still rife with using extreme scenarios to justify teaching high-risk restraint methods. The vast majority of violence encountered in care environments may be frightening, but it lacks the sophistication of the sort of violence encountered 'on the streets'. If people want to train for those situations, they are welcome to join a martial arts club.

In the context of all forms of care, including parents in their own home, there is a need for good de-escalation skills as opposed to learning a few simple 'Kung Fu' tricks. Every day around the world, vast numbers of people receive training in crisis management from a variety of training programmes who each claim that they base their physical skills training on applied research. The truth is that the evidence base for these programmes is crude at best (McDonnell, 2010). People will often learn physical methods that they forget as soon as they leave the classroom. The reality is that any physical skills taught in crisis management should be safe, effective and easy to remember. Simply, teaching less means learning more. Take a moment to consider what training could be like if it focused more on de-escalation rather than wasting time on physical skills.

This focus on extreme situations in training can be described as the 'What If?' game. People will describe a simple approach, followed by the question, 'What if the person has a knife?' This 'What If?' game is a highly dangerous process as it encourages people to think about extreme situations and catastrophise rare events. Here is a scenario that illustrates the danger of these extreme arguments:

'Imagine that you are suspended from a rope with a 1000 feet drop below you. You notice the rope is on fire and that there is a man with an axe stopping you from climbing back up the rope. It's a long way down. What do you do in this situation?'

This is not a serious example, and of course the real question is how you got yourself into that situation in the first place. The process of catastrophising creates a 'fear of fear' mentality, whereby any small situation can be exacerbated internally until it reaches a critical level.

When practicing a low arousal approach, there should be a strong focus on training for everyday situations. The training developed by Studio3 focuses on teaching simple de-escalation skills, and emphasises techniques for managing common, day-to-day events.

Trauma-Informed Behaviour Management

People in care environments may have either experienced or been exposed to trauma. 'Trauma-informed' services are not specifically designed to treat symptoms or syndromes related to sexual or physical abuse and other types of trauma, but they are informed about and sensitive to trauma-related issues present in survivors (Harris and Fallot, 2001).

Behaviour management approaches therefore need to account for the traumatised nature of the populations in their care. In intellectual disability services, trauma has been acknowledged as an important factor in the presentation of aggressive and violent behaviours. Person-centred approaches which acknowledge trauma and its effects (like the low arousal approach) tend to avoid the use of punitive consequences. It is hugely important to give people who present with behaviours of concern choices rather than boundaries (Pitonyak, 2005). Viewing an individual as 'traumatised' tends to alter our perception of their behaviour, and modify our responses to that behaviour. For example, if we understand that a person is 're-traumatised' every time they are restrained, it will help us to seek out alternatives.

Understanding the role that trauma plays in some individuals' everyday lives can make a huge difference to the care and support they receive. It is also very important to remember when working with victims of trauma that carers, staff and family members can also experience this trauma 'vicariously'. This means that exposure to someone who is highly stressed and traumatised can have a negative impact on oneself. In addition, seeing a person as traumatised can also help you to develop empathy towards that individual.

Trauma-informed care has become much more mainstream in recent years, and the concept of trauma-informed behaviour management is a natural extension of this idea. We often manage the behaviours of distressed individuals without thinking whether the seemingly effective strategies we use serve only to re-traumatise people further. Consider the example of Yohan:

'Yohan lives at home with his adopted family and has a diagnosis of ADHD. Yohan was a victim of neglect in his early childhood, and routinely witnessed violence in his family home. This culminated in a prison sentence for his father and his eventual removal from the family. His adoptive family initially found him difficult to control, and at times he escalated situations by becoming physically aggressive towards them. His adoptive father initially found himself imposing far too many boundaries and punishments. The use of sanctions, such as restricting time on his computer games and restricting his freedom of movement, appeared to manage his behaviour. The family received some additional training and support in low arousal approaches from Studio3, and realised very quickly that their overuse of boundaries and sanctions were actually re-traumatising Yohan. They did not get rid of all the rules, but did manage to eliminate the vast majority of them. They also began to consider the idea that Yohan was suffering from a form of PTSD.'

Physically restraining Yohan whilst he actively tried to escape from these holds undoubtedly retraumatised him by transporting him back to his first abusive family home. Good trauma-informed behaviour management has a simple guiding principle; when we work with someone who is highly stressed and often aggressive, we must avoid strategies that were used in their traumatic past. In many situations, we must teach alternative methods which allow the person to learn to self-regulate. We will describe later on in this book that, in some cases, allowing property destruction is better than restricting an individual. The most positive message of all is that most traumas will eventually heal.

If the behaviour of carers can inadvertently trigger violent and aggressive behaviours, then, logically, altering these triggering behaviours may have an impact on the management of violent and aggressive behaviours. It is useful for carers to engage in reflective practice, whereby they evaluate their performance in situations and learn from both positive and negative experiences (Schon, 1987). It is important to remember that all behaviour is meaningful, and to ask yourself why the person *needs* to engage in that behaviour. These types of thoughts may help carers to perceive the person as being less in control of their behaviour and view themselves as active contributors to the situation. In these circumstances, carers may think of solutions that focus on their own behaviour rather than manipulating the individual's behaviour.

Attempts have been made to explain how carers thoughts and beliefs affect their behaviour in care environments. Care staff may have negative thoughts about the behaviour of a person with autism spectrum disorder (ASD), such as, 'He causes so much trouble', which can directly affect their deeply held beliefs like, 'I can't cope with stress'. Altering these thoughts can help carers in their interactions with the people they are caring for.

Carers can bring their own personal experiences and learning history to care situations, which can be quite rigid and difficult to change. For example, care staff may hold the belief that people who misbehave should be punished, which might lead to them asking service users to write letters of apology after incidents. In such circumstances, the care staff is assuming that the individual was in control of their behaviour at the time of the incident. A more contemporary view is that some aggressive behaviour can be viewed as automatic, and may at times be out of the control of the person with autism (Richetin and Richardson, 2008).

Homeostatic Model of Arousal and Behaviour

Arousal has long been implicated with autism and behaviours of concern, and it is clear that a relationship exists between stress and arousal. It is important at this stage, however, to remember that an individual's level of physiological arousal influences the way that they process environmental sensory stimuli, and may also have a negative effect on human performance. Since some behaviours of concern are mediated by a heightened state of physiological arousal, the reduction of this arousal should reduce instances of behaviours of concern, at least in the short-term (McDonnell et al., 2014). Low arousal approaches are strategies used to manage such crisis situations. The primary goal of crisis management is 'arousal regulation'.

Emotional Contagion

Emotional contagion is an idea which means that emotions, both positive and negative, can spread from person to person and group to group (Elvén, 2010). This concept can be applied to supporting people in highly stressful situations. It is noteworthy that in neuroscience, 'mirror neurons' have become of increasingly greater interest to scientists. Mirror neurons are neurons that fire in harmony with other people. Whilst mirror neurons may be very important in the development of empathy, I believe that this concept has been over-used by researchers. In reality, understanding emotional contagion is crucial for any practitioner of the low arousal approach. Consider the following example:

'Fatima is a forty-four-year-old care worker who supports an adult with acquired brain injury (ABI). This older man is prone to explosive fits of rage, often without any obvious trigger. Fatima is one of six people who support this man in his home. The 'staff group' had decided to improve their communications by the use of shared text messages. It was discovered that many of these texts were highly emotive in nature, for example, "Just about survived that shift", was a fairly frequently expressed sentiment. In reality, there were very few incidents with this person. The texts inadvertently spread a negative and fearful message about the person. Fatima struggled to work with this individual as she found him stressful. She was advised to consult a psychologist regarding her stress at work. It was discovered that she had never experienced an extreme incident with

this man, but had read about other people's experiences through their vivid descriptions via text message.'

This is an example of negative emotional contagion. Fear spread amongst this staff team like wildfire. In the previous chapter on fear, it was made clear that low-frequency behaviours which are very intense can generate huge amounts of fear. Fatima worried every day when she began her shift and could not stop thinking about work when she returned home. It was a relatively easy process to reassure her that maybe the text message system needed to change. She was advised by her psychologist to text members of her group about positive interactions with this man (as there were, in fact, many).

Confident People Manage Stressful Situations Better

Training in the management of behaviour of concern has been associated with an increase in people's confidence (McDonnell, 2010; Allen and Tynan, 2000). People are often expected to work in highly stressful situations and try to appear both calm and confident. The low arousal approach creates high expectations among staff to appear confident. In a care situation, it only takes one member of a team to model a lack of confidence to other colleagues to create a vicious circle of fear. However, the opposite is also true: confident individuals can create an atmosphere of positivity and positive risk taking. Confidence has a clear link to other factors such as fear. When applying the low arousal approach, great care must be taken to avoid over-confidence. For example:

'Angela is a twenty-nine-year-old parent with four children. Her youngest son, Gordon, is a teenager. Gordon is continuously in trouble with the police, has been excluded from his school, and has recently, to use Angela's phrase, 'squared up to her'. Her husband,

who routinely works away from home, appears not to have any confrontations with his son. It became very clear that style of communication should be an important factor in managing Gordon's behaviour. Angela was provided training by members of the Studio3 training team in applying low arousal approaches. There was a strong emphasis on how to communicate clearly with Gordon in a calm but confident manner. Angela practiced these skills and was provided with mentoring when she applied the approach to her son. She was told to have very few rules, and to calmly enforce them. She was also advised never to argue with her son and to simply walk away.'

Appearing confident is so different from actually being confident. Angela found the approach very successful and at a one-year follow-up said that her relationship with Gordon had significantly improved. When asked to reflect about what was successful, she said, "I think I've changed my own behaviour, not my son's. And it may sound a little strange, but I think I'm much calmer, and I just don't worry about day-to-day issues".

Low Arousal Does Not Mean Doing Nothing

If there is one major misconception about the low arousal approach, it is that practitioners are essentially modern-day hippies who never enforce any rules and never push people. This is categorically a false assumption. Recently, I debated this point with my Swedish colleague Bo Heilskov Elvén, a well-renowned practitioner of the low arousal approach. Bo argues very strongly that there are many rules in society that all people have to follow. Someone who is stressed and traumatised can only focus on one rule at a time. If there is a constant theme in this book, it is that stressed people process information more poorly and therefore practitioners must be much more realistic about what a person can learn. Of course, people who are less stressed process information far more efficiently. So, how does this apply to the low arousal approach?

Firstly, having fewer boundaries does not mean having no boundaries at all. Sometimes it is our own behaviour that needs to be altered to reduce arousal. How you make requests, timing, and style is everything. Creating environments that are calm and reduce arousal is also going to help. There are also situations where rules may need to be followed for the health and safety of the person concerned. My colleague Andrea Page (PhD) has a special interest in applying low arousal approaches in healthcare environments. In her studies on clinical holding, Andrea has found that emergency-room nurses in the UK appear to have less crisis management training than in the past (Page et al., 2015). Young children who are highly stressed may injure themselves or even routinely have to attend an emergency department. In these circumstances, a low arousal approach can still be applied, for example when it comes to who is going to hold the child if they need to be sutured. Andrea's research has demonstrated that, in nearly 50% of situations, parents are asked to hold their child. When nursing staff were asked their reasons for this, there was an alarming response. Nearly half of her sample reported that parents knew their children better and find it easier to reduce their child's distress, whilst the other half of the sample maintained that if parents held their child and anything went wrong, it was not their responsibility. Andrea's work focuses on training nursing staff in how to create safe and calm environments for everyday procedures. It could be argued that in these circumstances, it is in the best interests of the child to receive treatment, but that this can still be done within a low arousal philosophy.

The Concept Becomes More Sophisticated

The current construct is much broader than the original collection of crisis management strategies. The evolution of the concept comes from a variety of sources. There are several key issues which have become much stronger themes, especially over the last 10-15 years. These include trauma-informed behaviour management, emotional contagion, and a much stronger emphasis on reflective practice. The approach has evolved to be much more than a collection of techniques employed when someone is 'melting down'. Rather, it has become a philosophical approach which places arousal-regulation at its very centre. Creating synchronous and harmonious interaction is an important aspect of the approach. My Belgian colleague Peter Vermeulen uses the expression 'neuro-harmony' to refer to a state in which your perspective is one of synchrony with other people (personal communication, 2018). It can be argued that a low arousal approach will mean increasingly focusing on creating harmonious interactions, even in the most extreme situations. There are, of course, strong parallels between the low arousal approach and the concept of Mindfulness. In essence, we are expecting people to stay in the moment and calm in situations that are almost the opposite. The reality is somewhat different. It is really incredibly difficult to consistently stay calm in highly stressful situations. If you can do this naturally, you are already an excellent practitioner of the low arousal approach, and probably quite a rare individual!

Despite people trying to convince us that all behaviour is learned, this book proposes a more complex view of behaviour. We will not always be able to identify triggers for behaviour, and sometimes causes are complex and difficult to define. It is important to be very balanced in this approach. Like a set of weighing scales, people should be aware of when things are out of balance. If people are too reactive, they can inadvertently escalate the situation. Before a person reaches full crisis, there is a window of opportunity where the arousal level of the individual is increasing and carers may intervene to avoid further escalation in behaviours. Typically, an individual will start to show behaviours at this stage of heightened arousal (e.g. pacing, shouting, self-injury).

In this pre-crisis phase, people will begin to notice changes in behaviour or mood that are unusual. This will almost certainly create a heightened sense of fear in supporters. In these circumstances, people become more questioning about a person's behaviour, and there is a real danger that people may overreact and become too 'solution-focused'. In my experience, many short-term changes in behaviours will, if left alone (and people do not react), begin to settle down. Sometimes, our 'well intentioned' interventions at this point may almost certainly escalate the situation. For the person being supported, we must always remember that they are trying to make sense of a world which is becoming more chaotic. This increases the individual's stress, and often leads to that person isolating themselves from people.

When we observe a change in a person's behaviour, we often try to evaluate risk. This is a survival mechanism. We are 'hardwired' to assess threats that may lead to harm. To survive in societies all over the world, there needs to be an understanding of risk. Unfortunately, this mechanism is not always reliable.

During phases of heightened arousal, we should always be as analytical as possible. It is really important, wherever possible, that we try to figure out why the person's behaviour appears to be changing. There are many different schools of thought which can be applied to analysing 'why' people behave in the way they do. I am aware that people reading this book will, by experience and learning, come from a variety of different backgrounds. It needs to be clear that human behaviour is complex, and that trying to provide an explanation for someone's behaviour does not necessarily mean that explanation is correct. The reality is that it is easier to support someone if we feel that we have some sense of an explanatory framework that we can relate to the person. The most dangerous situation for a group of staff is the prevalence of extreme views. These range from the general view that they do not know why the person behaves in this way, to a narrow, over-simplistic explanation.

If a group of supporters keep communicating to one another that they really do not know why a person behaves in the way that they do, this will often lead to increased levels of fear and helplessness within the group. People may begin to believe that the person is behaving in a manner that they cannot easily control. Consider the following example:

'Janet is a thirty-year-old support worker who is described as having a great relationship with a young man called Eoin. He is a looked-after child, and has described Janet as being like a big sister to him. In a period of approximately two months, Eoin's behaviour rapidly deteriorated. He became both verbally and physically aggressive towards Janet and pretty much all of his support staff. The staff team became extremely fearful. They held numerous meetings, which only seemed to increase their fear levels. One member of staff stated quite clearly, "We can't manage him anymore, he's too dangerous and unpredictable". The staff did manage to 'ride out the storm', and they discovered three months later that Eoin had developed a subtle and very rare form of epilepsy. This diagnosis really helped people to understand the explosivity and the suddenness of his behaviour. It also greatly helped Eoin to understand that he was not 'going crazy'. Although Janet maintained her relationship with Eoin, she did admit that the change in behaviour towards her was very frightening at the time, because she could not figure out why it was happening.'

This example shows how the lack of an explanatory framework combined with a sudden change in behaviour can be really difficult for supporters. It makes them feel unsafe and less in control of the situation. One difficult aspect of this work is the need to allow people to emotionally debrief (which we will discuss in a later chapter in more detail), balanced with the additional need of constraining people's emotions. In this example, increasing the frequency of staff meetings actually appeared to incubate the fear further. This is because each meeting ended without a clear shared understanding of 'why' Eoin was behaving in the way he was. When supporting people in these situations, practitioners, managers, and professionals must be very clear about the nature and purpose of such meetings. My recommendation is to distinguish between immediate debriefing to help people regulate their own emotions, and an analysis of the person's behaviour, where some kind of explanatory framework should be provided. It is OK to admit that a person is complicated and that we do not have all the answers. There is a strong bias in this book towards formulating and understanding people in terms of their stress. It is often better to provide a stress-based framework as it moves people away from over-simplistic diagnostic labels.

Narrow explanations also create difficulties. As a rule of thumb, if a group of staff come up with a simplistic explanation, it is usually likely to be wrong. Phrases such as 'they are doing it for attention' will usually lead to a construct described as 'malignant alienation' (Watts and Morgan, 1994). This is a term first used by therapists who described a process whereby they began to dislike their patients. Simplistic explanations which imply that a behaviour is deliberate (this includes words like 'targeting') will quite often lead to punitive consequences. There are some simple explanations which can be extremely helpful. I have found that one of the most common is that any increase in the intensity and frequency of behaviours of concern will almost certainly be related to specific health issues. A simple increase in temperature from a stomach bug can be dramatically amplified in the behaviour of someone who is distressed.

Sometimes there are very obvious triggers for someone's behaviour that we may understand and, with good intention, try to 'fix'. A huge factor in many people's lives is loneliness and lack of social support. When we are supporting people, it is difficult not to be overwhelmed by a person's isolation. The following example demonstrates that, whilst it is important that we try to fill this void, there can be unintentional side-effects. The following example shows how this can be a 'double-edged sword':

'Omar is a forty-six-year-old man with a history of being the victim of sexual and physical abuse. He has multiple, confusing diagnoses (including Schizoid Personality Disorder, Borderline Personality Disorder, Reactive Attachment Disorder). Omar has been subject to the 'revolving door' of living in a series of institutional settings, with bouts of living in the community. He is currently living in a supported living setting with specialist therapy and supports provided by members of a specialist team.

Omar had a difficult first three months living in his new home. In his words, the 'kindness' that people have shown him often cause him to think back to his past in a negative way. Omar has very little contact with his family, and very few people who could be described as his friends. His supporters realised that his behaviours of concern were increasing the closer he got to his birthday. After much reflection, they decided to organise a simple birthday in his house. This initially started really well, but Omar had hoped that his brother might attend, even for 10 minutes, which he did not. Omar managed about an hour before he started to become very emotional. After people left, he became upset and angry, but his staff supported him through this.'

With hindsight, the benefits of organising a birthday party far outweighed the costs of the party ending with Omar being distressed. It was important to show him that people cared about him, but sadly it also reinforced to him that he was still alienated from his family and that he had few friends. The low arousal approach adopted by his supporters was to keep the party short and brief. It was felt strongly that to not organise a small party would have probably been more difficult for him. It certainly increased empathy amongst his supporters.

If it is important to try to develop a shared understanding of why a person is behaving the way that they do, it is totally acceptable for people to formulate frameworks from their own perspectives. It can be really helpful for people who are more psychodynamically orientated to think about stress, trauma, attachment and loss as factors. Individuals with a stronger behavioural orientation may talk about more immediate analysis of behaviour in terms of reinforcement, and even use of the expressions 'functional assessment' and 'functional analysis'. Great care should be taken not to overanalyse situations. I was once a radical behaviourist, and in the early days I would never provide an analysis of someone's behaviour unless I had observed that individual for 20-30 hours. This practice stopped very quickly when it became clear that not all behaviours are equal. Some highly complex behaviours, such as self-injurious behaviour (SIB), require in-depth analysis, whereas for other behaviours, the information is readily available from talking to supporters.

Whatever your orientation or viewpoint, it is helpful to have some key questions that can help you to provide a framework. The pre-crisis checklist described below provides a set of questions that are useful for a staff team, individual practitioners or managers to answer as honestly as possible. Take 10-15 minutes now to think about a crisis situation that you may have experienced and answer these questions as honestly as possible. Try not to overanalyse your response to questions. It is often a good idea to answer the questions fairly rapidly, as often our intuition and 'gut feelings' have a part to play in this analysis.

	The Pre-Crisis Checklist	Yes	No
Physical Health	Have minor aliments been checked (migraines, gastric problems etc.)?		
Lack of Structure	Is the person resisting their normal routine?		
Lack of Predictability	Is the person less predictable? Are people over-estimating the risk of harm to themselves or others? Are people under-estimating the risk of harm to themselves or others?		
Stress	Is the person showing signs of stress?		
Trauma	Are there any significant life events or anniversaries that may contribute to this behaviour?		
Sensory Overload	Is the person avoiding sensory input and isolating themselves?		
Slow processing of information	Is the person struggling to focus on routine tasks?		

Poor attention and memory	Are there signs that the person is struggling to focus and remember everyday routines?		
Frustration	Is the person showing open signs of frustration and anger, even with simple tasks?		
Control	Is the person attempting to simplify and control their world?		
Emotional Contagion	Is the emotional impact of the behaviours affecting supporters of the person? Are people scared and frightened that the person will harm themselves? Are people scared and frightened that the person will harm supporters? Do any supporters appear to be angry with the person?		
Empathy	Are the supporters of the person struggling to empathise with them?		

	Is the person being supported not showing much empathy towards their supporters?		
Intent	Do people believe that the person is behaving in a planned or premeditated way?		
Excessive rules and boundaries	Are there too many rules in place for the person given their current behaviours of concern?		
People	Are supporters becoming more alienated from the person?		
Demands and Requests	Are supporters reducing demands and requests and simplifying the person's activities?		
Connection	Are some supporters struggling to make a connection with the person? Are there staff who believe that they are being targeted by the individual? Are there staff who clearly do not like this individual?		

	Do supporters have a shared understanding of this person's behaviour?		
	Has an episode like this occurred in the past?		
	Have there been any recent changes in routine - particularly changes of staff/supporters?		
	Is the weather or other seasonal changes having an impact on the behaviour?		
	Is this behaviour cyclical in nature?		

This exercise should help you come up with a framework for support. It is perfectly possible to then come up with a range of strategies that may help reduce the crisis. The reader must remember that many crises do not escalate into 'major meltdowns'. Given that we must be careful not to overreact to these situations, the following de-escalation strategies checklist may also be of help.

DSC De-escalation Strategies Checklist.

	Yes	No	Possible Options
Can we reduce stress in the person's immediate environment (noise, crowding, transitions etc)?			
Can we reduce decision-making for the person?			
If the sleep cycle is disturbed, how can we help to normalise this?			
Can we reduce the day-to-day demands of the programme?			
Can we increase cardiac exercise?			
Can we increase staff empathy for the person?			
Can we increase emotional support for staff?			
Staff			

Reassurance			
Can we simplify the person's world?			
Do not over-use distraction			
Do not carry on regardless			
Can we give the supporters a break?			
Can we give the person a break?			
Are there stress reduction strategies that have worked for this person in the past?			
Can we make the world as predictable as possible?			
Can we increase the person's sense of control over their environment?			
Can we simplify communication?			

Can we reduce fear in the supporters?			

The checklist should help to provide a series of strategies to reduce a person's overall stress and arousal. It is really vital that people still consider non-intervention as a strategy. If a person is not feeling well or there has been a change in the person's supports, a significant life event, or even health issues, providing a clear short-term plan and an explanatory framework may well be enough. However, there are times when the behaviour will escalate and supporters will experience a very difficult period. In the next chapter, we will concentrate on low arousal approaches to immediate crisis management, with some practical suggestions for how to 'ride out the storm'.

Key Learning Questions

1) Why is it important to apply a humanist philosophy to supporting vulnerable people?

2) What factors should you consider when evaluating a crisis situation?

3) What can YOU do to de-escalate crisis situations and help create a calm environment for distressed individuals?

4) How do you prepare yourself for working with a distressed person?

CHAPTER 11

RIDING OUT THE STORM

In the early part of this book, an analogy was used comparing a crisis situation to a ship experiencing a severe storm. In crisis circumstances, we have to ride out the storm and, to use a sailor's term, 'batten down the hatches'. You are not going to be able to prevent the storm, and there is no point in wishing it away. The primary focus is to keep everyone safe, stay mindful and focus on moment-to-moment factors within your control. It can be extremely scary to manage an angry and distressed person. Look at this picture. How does this image communicate hostility? Most people would describe this as someone who is communicating an aggressive intent with their entire body – for example the balled fists and intense eye contact.

We sometimes miss signs that a person is aggravated, or notice the signals too late. A good rule to follow is that most individuals who are distressed are usually extremely aroused at the time (leading to their reduced ability to process information). In these cases, we should avoid doing things that will further arouse this person. Or, to phrase it better, 'Don't add fuel to the fire'. There are many examples from the animal kingdom which show how we can communicate our emotions. The first person to really talk about this was Charles Darwin in his book '*The Expression of the Emotion of Man in Animals*' (1872). After 1872, Darwin recognised the power of non-verbal communication within all animal species. He was particularly fascinated by facial expressions. It is interesting to note that recent researchers have also indicated the importance of non-verbal facial expressions in conveying emotions.

A commonly used term in the training industry is the 'assault cycle' (Kaplan and Wheeler, 1983). In this model there is a triggering event, an escalation leading to a crisis point, recovery and something described as a post-crisis phase. This model represents a useful but overly-simplistic view of how behaviours can escalate. Behaviours can occur extremely rapidly, sometimes without an obvious triggering event, and this usually means that something internal to the person is happening. In addition, verbal aggression can lead to physical aggression, aggression towards objects, and even self-harm. However, the vast majority of verbal aggression (arguments, disputes, disagreements) actually do not escalate. Consider this exercise:

Think about an argument that you have had at home or at work in the last month. How did this situation de-escalate?

When you thought of your own examples in the above exercise, how analytical were you? Was it possible to figure out how you managed to de-escalate the argument? Sometimes we need to change our thinking processes even whilst we are arguing with people. In most cases, not responding can be the most effective intervention. I am not advocating that people should accept all forms of aggression, all of the time. However, in the moment when you are experiencing hostility, less is more. In situations where we experience fear, we will often overestimate risk. In the early chapters of this book we discussed 'fight, flight and freeze' responses. It is not unusual for people to become 'blunters' or even non-reactive in these situations. In a low arousal approach, anything you can do to minimise arousal is better. In this chapter, we will examine a whole range of practical strategies that can be useful in reducing arousal, and will help you to 'ride out the storm'.

Avoiding Arguments Is An Art Form

Avoiding arguments can be extremely difficult, and is significantly challenging to do in practice. However, it is a skill that you can practice. There are many individuals who find it difficult to avoid responding. This book is called *A Reflective Journey* because, to quote the famous psychiatrist Albert Kushlick at a conference in the 1980s, 'We are all fallible human beings'. We must not see the low arousal approach as a utopian fantasy in which we all behave wonderfully in every situation in our lives. Think about someone who is genuinely nice all the time - would you really like to have them as a friend? Or is it likely that you would find them irritating after a while? The reality is that good low arousal practitioners are honest individuals who strive to be aware of themselves and the people they support, not Mindfulness gurus or experts. The key to developing the ability to tolerate verbal abuse is to understand that this is a skill that needs constant updating. Good practitioners view incidents in an analytical and honest way. I was once approached at a conference a number of years ago by a family after doing a presentation on the low arousal approach. Two of the family members said that it was a very powerful day and that they had learned a lot. One of the parents said the following, "I bet you are a wonderful father, being such a kind and considerate man". I replied in a tongue-in-cheek manner, "I'm off duty when I'm at home". In truth, we need to be careful not to promote ourselves as paragons of virtue; we are human, and all humans are fallible.

Verbal Demand Reduction

Demand reduction in a crisis situation is a very poorly understood thing. In the previous chapter, we discussed reducing demands, requests and boundaries in general as a way to reduce stress. In a crisis situation, verbal demands and requests are often triggers to aggression, even though the intent may not be to escalate the situation. Actively listening and saying little is one key element. It is a really good idea to avoid filling in the spaces with words whilst someone is distressed. Many individuals find it extremely uncomfortable to be passive if someone is verbally swearing and screaming at them. Try to avoid arguing with the person, even if you believe that the individual is in the wrong. Here is a day-to-day example:

'A businesswoman who was having a very stressful day reversed her car into a stationary car, but did not appear to cause external damage. The male in the stationary car got out and started to shout and scream "What the f*** did you do that for?" The woman apologised and focused on whether there was any damage caused. She did not tell the man to calm down or argue with him; rather, she modelled calmness. The situation appeared to calm very rapidly as there was no obvious damage. Though the woman felt angry when

the man shouted at her, she knew herself to be in the wrong. For a split second, she thought she was going to react aggressively. However, it became very clear that role modelling calmness would have a more positive impact in this situation.'

Staying Calm Exercise

Now you have read the above example, try to think of a situation that you may have experienced in your life which involved someone being verbally hostile towards you. If you can, try to remember what you did, what you were thinking, and what you were feeling. To be really reflective (and not everyone can do this), think of a situation that you handled poorly by becoming angry or upset. What have you concluded from this exercise? Are you a person who can consistently demonstrate self-regulation and control? Staying in calm in a crisis situation is something that can be practiced. There are many wide-ranging examples in which a calm response to a crisis helped to defuse the situation. One of the best examples took place on the RMS Titanic in April 1912. After the ship struck the iceberg, there was a realisation that there were insufficient lifeboats to save all of the passengers and crew. We know from historical accounts that Second Officer Lightoller behaved calmly and stoically in this situation. He made sure that all women and children got off the ship first. Incredibly, he appeared to remain calm whilst facing certain death. Teaching self-control and self-regulation is a crucial part of 'riding out the storm'.

Non-Verbal Requests

One of the key strategies to remember is that, in the care context, you are dealing with someone who is stressed and traumatised, who is therefore not efficiently processing what you are saying to them.

Making requests of people when they are highly aroused and stressed can be a hugely risky undertaking. Remember that requests do not have to be negative - you might ask someone if they want a cup of tea or if they would like to go for a walk. However, when a person is overwhelmed, they cannot fully process these simple requests and make clear decisions. I first developed the following expression in training: 'When in doubt, shut your mouth. If you're not sure, walk out the door'.

For people who are verbal, and especially those who are non-verbal, simplifying communication is critical. In crisis situations or when someone is experiencing 'meltdown', it is sometimes easier for them to process a non-verbal request or gesture. For example:

'Fleur is a sixteen-year-old teenager with a severe to moderate intellectual disability. Fleur can sometimes become very aggressive extremely rapidly. Her teaching staff have noticed that she will cover her ears, break furniture, and often try to escape from her classroom setting. They find that saying nothing and holding her jacket up gives her the cue to leave the room when she starts to become distressed.'

We process non-verbal information much more efficiently than we do verbal communication, especially if it is a simple request. In the previous example, we stated that we should avoid asking people for things that require a decision. Using a non-verbal approach would mean that instead of asking someone if they would like a drink, you simply make them a drink and leave it near them without saying a word. Whilst we talk about their importance, it is surprising how rarely non-verbal requests are actually used in practice. A focus on non-verbal communication can really help a distressed individual figure out what is being asked of them.

Non-Verbal Guidance; or, The 'Pied-Piper' Method

There are many situations in which an individual can become distressed in a public setting or a confining space within their home. The 'Pied-Piper' Method is a technique that I use with staff to encourage distressed individuals to move to a safer, quieter or calmer area. This is achieved by a member of staff opening a door or walking outside themselves, and in many situations, the individual who is distressed will naturally follow them. This is all achieved without any verbal communication. It is important that no physical contact is used with this strategy. Whilst this method does not guarantee success, people who are hyper aroused become highly sensitised to any verbal interaction. Using your body to communicate the message will therefore be more effective and less confrontational than telling someone to stay calm. This approach is most effective when you have already established a positive relationship with the individual.

Distraction and Diversion

When someone is hyper aroused and angry, we often try to distract those individuals. This type of strategy is amazing when it is successful, but if it is used too much in a situation, it will often create more confusion within the person you are supporting, and can actually increase their arousal.

A common diversionary strategy, especially for people in older adult or acquired brain injury (ABI) services, is to distract them by engaging in conversations about childhood memories, as these memories often tend to be the most robust and reliable. Consider Agnes in this example:

'Agnes is an eighty-eight-year-old woman with a diagnosis of dementia. She lives in a care home with 60 other people. Her supporters have observed a decline in her behaviour over the years. She becomes confused very quickly, and often accuses other residents of stealing her possessions. Staff have found that both reassuring her and debating with her seem to escalate her arousal. They finally learned to distract her by bringing in a photo album of her childhood memories and showing them to her. They found that, most of the time, she would forget what she was initially distressed about, and instead focus on the childhood memories.'

Technology can also be a useful tool for distracting people. We will often use computer games or an engaging hobby or interest (such as chess, or other games that require concentration) to stop people from thinking about something distressing. Physical activities can also be helpful.

There are many ways to develop distraction and diversion strategies. However sometimes a successful diversion strategy can be misinterpreted, like in the following example:

'Douglas is a fifty-two-year-old man who has been diagnosed with a personality disorder and suspected borderline learning disabilities. He can sometimes become 'fixated' on a particular topic or subject. Whilst walking with two friends and one member of his support staff one day, he threatened to run across a busy road if he couldn't get an ice cream. The support staff member was clearly worried, and offered him an ice cream after they visited one more place first (which was not near a main road). The staff member bought all of the individuals an ice cream, but upon returning to the group home

was chastised for 'giving in' to Douglas. More seriously, they were told to record the incident as a 'near miss'.'

This member of support staff acted in a manner befitting the Low Arousal Approach. When does successful diversion become interpreted as a 'near miss'? Instead, we should think about recording situations of successful diversion, as it demonstrates the effectiveness of our behaviour management strategies. Terms such as 'near miss' are highly negative, and can create a culture of fear. We might say a person is doing very well because distraction and diversion works, or we can re-frame it as 'this person is having lots of near misses'. Which is more beneficial?

This example also highlights a perceived difficulty with distraction. Often the most powerful and immediate distraction strategies involve food, cigarettes, or some other kind of immediate reward. People have almost been conditioned to view the use of rewards in crisis situations as potentially reinforcing bad behaviour. This is a completely understandable but incorrect view of reinforcement. In a crisis situation, you should use the most powerful distractions you have available, regardless of whether it is reinforcing or not. If it comes down to restraining a person or letting them have an ice cream, choose the path of least resistance. Good behaviour management means the safe management of a situation by any reasonable means.

Managing Environmental Triggers

When a person is stressed or in a state of hyperarousal, they become highly sensitive to all sensory experiences in their environment. Whilst it is true that sensory sensitivity is widely understood by researchers in the autism field, sensory sensitivity is also common in people with a variety of other conditions. Managing environmental sensory triggers is therefore very important when a person is distressed. The first way to do this is to reduce sensory stimulation in the immediate environment. In a person's home, we may turn off music or televisions. We may also remove ourselves from their immediate line of sight. In fact, many staff who are trained in low arousal approaches tend to find that they spend considerable time sitting in their cars or a garden area when supporting people in their own homes.

This should not be confused with secluding or isolating an individual in a room or safe area. In my experience, most of the individuals I have worked with do not find forced isolation pleasant – in fact, they find it traumatising. How many people request to freely enter a seclusion room without struggling or showing signs of distress? In group home situations, people often want to retreat to their own room as they feel safe there, but a bedroom should never be used for forced isolation, for both moral and practical reasons.

Avoidance of environmental stimuli that people find irritating is extremely important in this critical phase between high arousal and meltdown. We have all learned to avoid places that are too crowded, too noisy or too hot. We may simply avoid entering these settings, or escape them once they become intolerable. Escape from noise, crowding and excessive stimuli are all important factors in managing aggressive behaviour, as individuals who are distressed are more hypersensitive to any form of sensory stimulation.

Consideration should always be given to using safe places (usually where there are few people) so that an individual may feel less confined. Traditional behaviour management approaches tend to focus on confining people rather than taking them to safe and quiet spaces, and in many situations, this has an arousal-increasing effect. Consider the following example:

'Tina is a teenage girl living in a group setting with other individuals who have been victims of sexual or physical abuse. Tina's behaviour takes the form of physical aggression towards her support staff and deliberate self-harm. Her behavioural issues warranted an increase in her staffing to one-on-one input, pretty much 24 hours a day. Tina often becomes distressed later in the evening, telling people that she does not want to have her recurring bad dreams and nightmares. Tina's safe space late at night is to be driven in a car. Her new routine involves being taken out for a long drive from 7 o'clock in the evening until approximately midnight. This routine occurs even in a normal school week. Tina particularly likes the ocean, and it is not usual for this drive to take an hour and half to a particular spot where she can sit and watch the ocean with her support staff. Her staff team weighed the benefits of this, considering that she normally doesn't get to sleep until 3am with the fact that this method helps her

get to sleep by 1am most nights. This is also a fantastic opportunity for her to talk to someone about why her dreams bother her.'

Another bonus to this strategy is that the other individuals in her group home tend to be much more relaxed in Tina's absence. On the other hand, some of them complained that Tina was being rewarded for her bad behaviour. This was addressed by making sure that everyone had at least a small amount of quality one-on-one time in the week.

Awareness of Non-Verbal Behaviours as a Trigger for Aggression

The more stressed people become, the more threatened they can be by even the smallest instructions or requests. People can become frightened of their support staff very rapidly. In heightened states of stress and arousal, they can often misinterpret simple movements. The most common method of communication is predominately non-verbal; therefore, we need to be aware of the signals that we are mostly unconsciously communicating to the people we are supporting. The following are some simple non-verbal signs that you can send to a distressed individual:

1) Appear Calm

Appearing calm is not the same as having an inner sense of calm. If there is one really important skill that a person must try to learn, it is to appear calm to people who are distressed. We are attempting to create a calm atmosphere, and it is critical that we are good role models of calmness. Throughout this book, the concept of emotional contagion has been repeatedly mentioned. People who exude an air of calmness can often transmit this to other people. A close friend of mine, who is a serving police officer, told me that he has used the low arousal approach many times in his career. Whilst he would argue that no method can be 100% successful in all situations, the most important factor is that the more often you respond in a calm manner to people in hostile situations, the more confident you will appear.

Our awareness of our own body language can be quite poor, especially when we are stressed and in a high state of arousal. It is really important to avoid tensing muscles and try to breathe slowly and regularly. Look at the following picture. A simple strategy for helping you to relax and appear calm is to lower your arms and open your fingers.

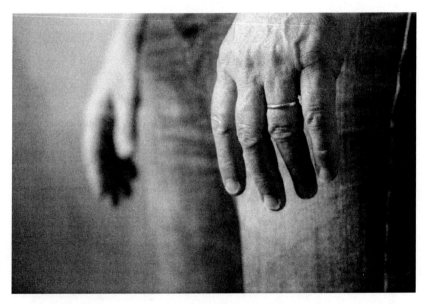

2) Avoid Direct Eye Contact

Direct eye contact can be extremely arousing, and can often evoke a strong fear response, especially in distressed people. Please stare at the picture below for 10 seconds. How does it make you feel? Does it make your heart race faster?

Now look at this picture for 10 seconds.

You will notice a very large difference in your emotional responses to both of these images. Did you notice that the person in the second image seems to be staring into space? Did it make you think differently about this individual?

Generally, it is difficult not to stare at someone who is 'making a scene'. When you are in a situation where someone is melting down, try to avoid staring and instead maintain regular, intermittent eye contact.

3) Be Wary of Physical Touch

Touch can be a sign of warmth and affection, but it can also be a sign of threat and hostility. Physical contact increases physiological arousal, such that your heart beats faster and you become more alert as your adrenaline and cortisol increases. This has survival value, as animals who are captured by predators can receive sufficient energy and adrenaline to escape. Touch can also increase levels of particular hormones, such as oxytocin. The important thing to remember is that touch will be rapidly interpreted by a person who is distressed. Whilst you may be trying to calm an individual down, what is important is how the person perceives your touch, whether

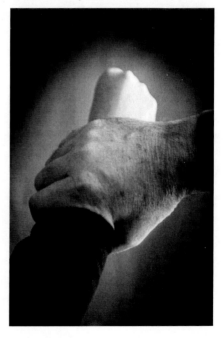

the intent is hostile or not. If they are highly stressed, they are more likely to view you as someone with a hostile intent. So many people we support are used to being handled or held in particular manner, so it is natural for them to become even more stressed when physical contact is made.

Many people are very sensitive to being touched, particularly on their forearms. The reality is that this is often a precursor to some kind of physical restraint or force. In the previous chapter, we discussed trauma-informed behaviour management. In this vein, we must try to avoid physical contact which could indicate to the distressed individual that similar restrictive holds are about to be used. A key part of the Low Arousal Approach is the avoidance of physical restraint, which also means removing the threat of restraint from the people we support's environment, thus allowing them to heal from the previous trauma of restraint.

4) Slow Your Movements Down

A general guide is to move slowly and cautiously around someone who is clearly threatened and distressed. When we move rapidly, we cannot necessarily outrun or outsmart people. We should also think about what we are communicating to people when we do this. Moving slowly, on the other hand, can create a sense of calmness. It is well documented that in escape situations, for example from airplanes or burning buildings, people are told to walk slowly for a good reason. It is not just that it is safer and will cause fewer injuries; it also creates a sense of calmness. There are many examples in which an individual's calm demeanour has prevented panic from ensuing. There are individuals we support who, when in a hyper aroused state, will interpret any movements towards them as hostile.

This is an automatic process which takes place in the primal limbic system in the brain, and is not always a conscious response, as the following example demonstrates:

'Graham is twenty-four-years old and lives in a supported living setting. Graham has Down's Syndrome, and frequently seeks out physical contact from his support team. Graham became very distressed when he heard the news that his mother had died from a member of staff. The support staff who broke the news reached forward to tenderly touch him on the shoulder, but Graham appeared startled and slapped her across the face.'

We can only speculate as to why Graham had this startled and unusual response. In this situation, it is likely that Graham was in a state of hyperarousal. This led to him almost instinctively interpreting the comforting touch as a sign of threat, rather than a positive indicator of warmth and affection.

This processing would all have occurred within split seconds in the primal part of his brain. There is no doubt that the member of staff's intention was to gently touch Graham on the shoulder, communicating warmth, kindness and empathy.

Can we still touch people and show affection? The answer is of course 'yes'. There are many ways of doing this, the most obvious being to ask the person, "Is it OK if I touch you?" or "Do you want a hug?" The key is to indicate to the person what you are going to do in a calm and gentle manner. In other situations, slowly describing what you are going to do will help the person feel less threatened. You might say, "I'm going to sit next to you, OK?". All of this prepares people so that they are less likely to have a scared or stressed reaction. Our relationship with the individual is also very important. If you have known a person for a while, then touch is perfectly fine and appropriate. However, the less you know the person, the more wary you should be of touching them when they are in a state of high arousal.

5) Be Aware That Gestures Can Be Misinterpreted

Gestures are a natural part of human communication. We often use them to exaggerate a point we wish to make. Understanding that gestures can be misinterpreted by individuals is very important. For example, there are a number of gestures in European countries that are not universal. If you give a thumbs up in the UK to someone, it usually means you're doing well, or saying 'well done'. However, in certain European countries, showing someone your thumb is an insult. Gestures are culturally relative.

Studies have shown that individuals vary in their use of gestures. Have a look at the image below and try to interpret what this gesture means.

The majority of individuals would interpret this as an open, communicative gesture. The person may be making a point in what would be described as a non-threatening manner. In the next example, look at the posture of the person, and think about what they are communicating.

This image communicates a closed posture, where the person usually does not want to make eye contact and will turn their back on you. They key message is that postures and gestures are a huge part of communication. Take the following as an example:

'Jasper works with vulnerable children. He is a trainer in the low arousal approach, but feels he still has some work to do as he often uses gestures to communicate with the children that he supports. After a particularly difficult situation, he realised that he had been pointing his finger at a child who grabbed his arm and bit it. It was definitely not his intention to appear threatening. In fact, Jasper's relationship with this young man was particularly excellent, and he had been joking with him. After discussing the situation with the young man, it would appear that the behaviour of concern was a reaction to perceived threat.'

Gestures are a very powerful form of communication, and therefore can also be used very effectively to manage crisis situations. In some situations, using gestures alone without spoken language can be extremely powerful. This is because distressed individuals will be processing information much more slowly, as their brain will be in 'alert mode'.

The gesture looked something like the image on the left, but was probably interpreted by the young person as something similar to the image on the right:

Consider the next example:

'Neil is sixty-two years old. He suffered major head trauma in a car crash 6 years ago. He has physically recovered, but now has huge short-term memory issues and what could be described as 'panic attacks', which he finds very distressing. He can become distressed very rapidly, but he also calms down very quickly. Neil becomes confused over relatively simple requests, which can lead to physical aggression. The most common crisis situations often occur in the mornings when he is washing and dressing himself. This is normally a very slow process, and he will often become frustrated and angry that he struggles with such simple, everyday tasks. In recent months, things have dramatically improved. His wife noticed that it was best to not speak to him at all in these situations. It is better to use 'calming gestures', and if he needs directions to use gestures only.'

By reducing verbal demands and instead quietly indicating that she is there to help if he needs her, Neil's wife was able to reduce his levels of stress and agitation in these moments.

6) Avoid Gathering Staff in Crisis Situations

In many different crisis management training programmes, it is often suggested that support staff should band together to deter an individual. This suggestion is completely counter to a low arousal approach. In crisis situations, carers can find it supportive to have other people around as it tends to make them feel safe. The paradox is that it will often increase the stress level of the individual. The more people who are witness to your actions, the greater the likelihood that your stress levels will increase. Studies in psychology have demonstrated an effect called social facilitation, more commonly known as the 'audience effect', whereby people tend to behave very differently when they have an audience (Strauss, 2002). Many people find being watched during stressful situations very difficult.

This strategy of gathering onlookers only works if it is intended to intimidate the distressed person. We often ask staff to gather as it increases our own sense of safety and confidence. If there are too many people in the vicinity of the person, they may struggle to understand who is communicating with them. Therefore, if you have a second person, they should be silent and, ideally, out of the immediate line of sight of the person who is aroused and distressed. In circumstances where people do gather, it is very important that they do not attempt to intervene, as this is likely to confuse the person. Well-intentioned colleagues may 'rush in' or talk too much to the individual. The general rule is that a second or even third person should only become involved when they have been requested by the person who is leading the incident.

7) Remove Other People From the Situation

Audience effects can also occur when other people and outsiders gather to watch someone who is distressed. People tend to find it distressing and potentially traumatising to watch individuals who appear to be angry or shouting. In many care home settings, you do not get to choose who you live with, which often leads to interpersonal disputes. Witnessing a person's behaviour escalate can be a frightening experience. People can become traumatised very easily when they witness another person's trauma. Paradoxically, it can also be fascinating for people. 'Rubbernecking' is term often used to describe the behaviour whereby people in crowds extend their necks to get a better view of a situation. Early in my career, I worked with an individual with severe learning disabilities who rarely left his room in a hospital. It was decided that he would go on a day outing to the seaside, which was generally a positive experience. A member of staff who was incredibly positive agreed to work with me on this outing. Near the very end of the day, as we returned to the coach, I noticed that the individual in my care was punching himself, and that I could not see the other member of staff. When I looked around, I saw the member of staff lying on the pavement, holding the side of his head. The individual we were supporting had made an involuntary side wards head movement, catching my co-worker in the head. Both people managed to recover from the situation very quickly, however a crowd of 'rubbernecks' had gathered around them. Interestingly, none of these people offered to help. My colleague and I, who were very embarrassed, describe what happened afterwards very differently. I recall asking the crowd politely, "Please move on, as it will upset this young man further". My colleague claims that I told them all to "Clear off!" All memory is, of course, subjective.

In all forms of care settings, when people become distressed in group situations, we often try to remove them as a method of defusing the situation. Applying the low arousal approach, removing onlookers should be a priority. School staff often have this dilemma when they have a disruptive pupil, like Hamish:

'Hamish attends a residential school for children with behavioural issues. He has been diagnosed with ADHD and 'conduct disorder', and more recently dyslexia. He struggles to focus on staff in classrooms. When he finds a task difficult, he will often become argumentative and aggressive towards his teachers. In the past, they used to remove him from the situation. However, a number of teachers had been hurt doing this, usually by having objects thrown at them. There are 6 other pupils in his class, two of whom argue with him whilst the other four appear to be scared and frightened. Watching Hamish when he is shouting and swearing is a traumatising experience for these other pupils. The teachers decided on a new evacuation drill. This is similar to a fire drill whereby, on the use of a key word, everyone leaves the room with the exception of one teacher and Hamish. Hamish often calms down once the audience is removed.'

In the above example, the disruption caused to the classroom by Hamish's behaviour was diminished by removing onlookers from the situation, which actually had the effect of reducing the length of Hamish's episodes. The low arousal approach does not advocate for behaviour management strategies like crowd gathering which use subtle forms of coercive control. It is always better if a person can be given the time and space to calm down with an individual that they know and trust.

8) Keeping Your Distance

Space and aggression are linked in a number of complex ways. Animal studies consistently demonstrate that overcrowding can lead to aggressive behaviour (Calhoun, 1962). The amount of space you require can vary from situation to situation. People may accept that they have to travel on crowded buses, trains, and aircrafts, and, to a certain extent, they can prepare themselves in anticipation of these situations. In addition, we can 'tune out' in situations where our focus is more on watching a movie, concert, or sporting event. Our brains effectively filter out 'threat signals' in many of these situations. However, for all of us, our behaviour is still determined by social context. You would struggle if someone you did not know very well sat very close to you. We can sometimes invade a person's space as a form of social control.

The social rules about distances can vary. It used to be thought that different cultures had different average preferred social distances for people they know and for strangers. More recent research has identified how complicated these relationships can be, influenced by factors such as age, gender and the climate you live in (Sorokowski et al., 2017). People who live in warmer climates appear to stand closer and make more physical contact in comparison to people in colder climates. The most important thing is that the space surrounding them is really important for anyone who is highly stressed. It is critical to be very aware that our use of space can have a positive or negative influence. In a crisis situation, a low arousal approach would suggest that we need to be aware of not invading a person's space.

There is a significant body of research which demonstrates that standing close to an individual will increase physiological arousal. Most people in typical, interpersonal communication (though this is culturally relative) will stand not much closer than 3 feet, and  certainly no closer than 18 inches. Cinemas and theatres are great examples of these social rules. If you are sitting next to a stranger in a side-by-side seat, you will avoid physical contact at all costs (unless you have an alternative agenda). When a person is in a state of heightened arousal, they become more aware of the space that surrounds them. There are studies which demonstrate that 'body buffer' zones can vary between groups. Kinzel (1970) identified through observation that prisoners who were labelled as 'violent' appeared to become more aggressive if people entered their 'buffer zone'. A recent study identified that the social distances of children with autism were greater than a control group of children (Candini et al, 2016). There are huge individual differences in preference. Most importantly, the 'threat zone' appears to increase the more a person becomes physiologically aroused.

Try the following self-awareness exercise. Think of a person you support or know very well, and ask yourself the following questions:

1) In normal conversation, how close do I sit with them?

2) Does the person appear to be ok with closer proximity and light touch (i.e. slight touch on shoulder etc)?

3) Does the person seem to actively avoid sitting or standing too close?

4) Does the person say that they do not like their space to be invaded?

5) Do they have any fear of confined spaces?

When you think of your answers, was it relatively easy to think about physical distances that the person would find comfortable? People who are highly stressed and hypervigilant are more likely to require more interpersonal distance. People with severe learning disabilities will often indicate very clearly non-verbally if you enter their space. Take the following for example:

'Barry is a nineteen-year-old man who has the label of autism with 'strong sensory features'. His verbal communication skills are similar to a very young person, but his understanding of spoken language is good. He currently attends a specialist service during the day, which has a high level of staffing specifically for him. It was observed that he found it hard to tolerate too many people in his immediate line of sight. He also can become distressed in noisy and

unpredictable environments. His service is relatively new, and encourages a low arousal approach. This has led to people actively avoiding overexposing him to crowded environments and, most importantly, staff being aware that he must have control of his immediate environment. He was visited by an Occupational Therapist who very carefully introduced herself to him. Barry guided her quite gently to the door and said a word that sounded like 'Go'. Under the new low arousal approach, this was encouraged as it helps to give him a sense of control over his environment.'

In this example, the behaviour is understood in terms of Barry's need to feel in control due to the fact that his arousal levels increase when his space is invaded. Having a new person (no matter how well-trained they are) leave his environment reduced the frequency of distressed incidents quite dramatically. Prior to this experience, he would have been discouraged from this 'behaviour' as it was perceived as rude. Understanding that stressed individuals need more space is critical to the low arousal approach. A simple rule to apply, especially if you do not know the person, is to keep the distance between you to between 2 to 3 metres. Watch out for non-verbal signs (loud vocalisations, gestures that indicate to you to leave the room, the person leaving your line of sight to avoid you) and avoid invading the person's space. It is often the case that Studio3 low arousal practitioners spend most of their time maximising interpersonal distance when a person is highly stressed.

9) Be Aware of the Power Messages You Communicate

Frightened and stressed individuals are more hypervigilant, and it is really important to make ourselves non-verbally and verbally non-threatening. We have already discussed slowing movements down, avoiding direct eye contact, and other immediate strategies. However, in my experience, especially when working with children, we may present unintentionally in quite a threatening manner. Look at the following picture, and notice how the adult has not only invaded the young person's space, but they are also looking down on them from a height. Whether it is the adult's intention or not, this will be a frightening image for the young person.

This principle does not just apply to adults working with young children. It is very easy to communicate aggression and hostility. I remember working with a member of staff who was middle-aged, five-foot-tall and female, who was blissfully unaware that her arms folded posture, foot tapping and general non-verbal demeanour was very scary. It was interesting that she was unaware of how powerfully she presented to people in crisis situations.

On a positive note, if we are aware of our 'non-verbal signature', it can sometimes be relatively simple to do something about it. Look at the following image and note the difference in the power relationship conveyed by the adult in comparison to the first image.

10) Tactically Withdrawing from the Person

This strategy is slightly different from the earlier example of Hamish in his classroom. When a person is stressed and their behaviour is escalating to a meltdown, we often do not remove ourselves from a situation quickly enough. By the time we realise that our 'line of sight' presence is escalating arousal and stress, a meltdown may be inevitable. It is important to be aware that sometimes the simple act of withdrawing from a situation can lead to a decrease in physiological arousal. Oftentimes, people become involved in arguments, leading to increased frustration. In my opinion, many arguments can continue for much longer than they need to, and this increases arousal and stress for all people concerned. If you cannot resolve an argument, or a person fails to follow a request, somebody needs to back down in order to defuse the situation. That should nearly always be the person who is a position of power:

'Clarice is thirty-six years old, and has Asperger's Syndrome. When she is stressed, she often isolates herself in her room and avoids speaking to her family. Her parents regularly try to communicate with her, but they also find it frightening and difficult. They worry that the more she isolates herself, the worse her situation will become. Upon reflection, they admitted to having tried a wide range of approaches. These included telling her to join them for dinner, offering her rewards to sit with them, and making mealtimes her choice. It eventually transpired that situations often escalated when they invited her to come down for dinner, usually followed by knocking on her bedroom door, with a gradual increase in what they described as 'firmness'.'

The fact that Clarice's parents loved her and wanted to help her is both laudable and understandable. However, as matters escalated, their descent into arguments only led to poor outcomes; namely that Clarice rarely ate with them, and there became an overarching sense of frustration within the home. The advice that they applied from a low arousal practitioner was to recognise the escalation while it was occurring, and to try and stop themselves from arguing with her when she did not respond to their polite requests. This had mixed outcomes. Her mother admitted that she 'struggled to stop herself' once she started to argue with Clarice, and that this was usually followed by swearing and other abusive language in response. Eventually, after positive practice, the family managed to understand that, at the point when an argument was about to occur, they should walk away. They eventually managed to do this much more successfully, which in turn led to an improved relationship with their daughter. The key issue was that, by backing down first, her parents felt like they were 'letting her win'. Once it was clear that avoiding the argument at all was far more positive than her parents 'winning', good changes occurred.

The reality is that 'backing away' from a dispute is easier to do in theory than in practice. Here is another example:

'Matthew is forty-four years old and detained in a secure facility due to many years of 'risky behaviours'. He has multiple labels which include Borderline Personality Disorder, Schizophrenia and Bi-Polar Disorder. His support staff often use physical restraint to de-escalate his behaviour. Matthew is highly verbally aggressive, mostly towards staff. His written support plan, agreed by a multi-disciplinary team, contained a set of 'traffic light' warnings corresponding to increases in his threatening behaviour. This quite often seemed to escalate his arousal, and routinely led to physical restraint from his support staff. During these restraints, there was clear evidence of injury to the staff team attempting to apply restraint. The Studio3 solution was to tell them that restraint was no longer an option, and the escalating warnings were eradicated. Instead, staff have been encouraged to 'actively ignore' Matthew's abusive behaviour. He has also been told that he can request to walk in the grounds if he feels angry and frustrated, with his support staff shadowing him from a distance.'

In Matthew's situation, there were too many rules surrounding him, and he clearly struggled to regulate himself after receiving verbal warnings from staff. The staff were divided on whether the traffic light system actually worked in practice. One of them stated that it worked in theory, but that they would end up restraining him at least 30 percent of the time after the final warning was given. The real clue came from a member of staff who said, "After we restrain him, we usually take him for a walk in the grounds under supervision, where he can walk quite freely, smoke a cigarette and calm down". The solution was simply to offer this calming down period *before* the situation escalated to the need for restraint.

These 10 simple ways of decreasing the physical and non-verbal demands upon distressed individuals are simple concepts to understand, but far more difficult to apply when you yourself are highly aroused. Being aware of how eye contact, posture, body language and physical proximity can be perceived by a distressed individual is the first step to becoming a calmer and less non-verbally threatening practitioner. In highly stressful situations, we must sometimes be the person who 'gives in'. That can involve allowing someone to escape from a situation in a planned manner. For many people, this can 'go against the grain' of what they have been taught to do in crisis situations.

Facilitating Planned Escape

The most under-used strategy to manage high risk behaviours and avoid physical restraint is to allow the person to escape in a planned manner. In the example of Matthew, the escape strategy eventually occurred over a lengthy, time consuming process. People who are highly stressed can experience a flight reaction when they are highly aroused, and this means that they will often try to escape from situations. Facilitating ways for a person to escape to a safe place, in a planned manner, is a key part of the low arousal approach. The following example occurred in a school for younger children:

'Alexandra is an eight-year-old girl with a recent diagnosis of ADHD and suspected dyslexia. She has already been excluded from three schools due to 'absconding' and running out of the classroom into the street (fortunately, her current school is in a suburban area with little traffic). It has been noted that she will often smile when she does this. One teacher describes her as a 'lovable little dynamo'; another as 'a real handful'. The behaviour was occurring at a high frequency (3 to 4 times a day), even when staff were vigilant. There was naturally a genuine concern for her safety. Initially, they showed her a safe room within the school that she could run to if she wanted to escape. She was also allowed to say 'No' if she did not want to continue with her lessons. After a period of experimentation, she still seemed to prefer running out of the main door of the school! Eventually, a cheap tent was placed outside in the small play area, which had one main access point. This was described to her as her 'calming zone', and was far more effective in practice than the designated safe room.'

Whilst the planned escape area appeared to help Alexandra regulate her behaviour, this was only the start of further positive strategies, including increased cardiac exercise (3 x 15 minute slots per day), simplification of her curriculum and a shared understanding amongst her supporters that she was developmentally quite young. Whilst her behaviours were most likely related to stress and a need for escape, it was also acknowledged that, on a few occasions, she found the routine entertaining. This suggested that she was under rather than over-stimulated. Planned escape is the preferred option of my colleague Gary LaVigna, who is a worldwide expert in proactive approaches to managing behaviour, and is also well-known for the development of crisis management strategies with his colleague Tom Willis from the Institute of Applied Behaviour Analysis in California. They often use phrases such as 'planned escape' and 'strategic capitulation' to focus people on the use of avoidant strategies in crisis management. In my early research, I was greatly influenced by this work. The approach has a sound premise, which is that highly stressed people often need to escape from situations, and that allowing them to do so in a safe manner is good crisis management. Obviously, in the longer term, trying to create situations that do not escalate the person's behaviour to the point where they feel the need to escape is a crucial part of the equation. Planned escape will often increase a person's sense of control over their environment. This does not just apply to people in care and school-type environments. It can be argued that most of the readers of this book will have used their own planned escape strategies from difficult or uncomfortable situations.

Unplanned Escape

Unplanned escape is a situation feared by most organisations. When working with vulnerable children and adults, we often fear that they will come to harm if unsupervised. Organisations have a duty of care to keep the people they support safe, and many organisations and families have a planned response to people 'running away'. In these situations, effective analysis of risk is really important. The following example really illustrates the point that accurate information is required:

'Sandra is a young woman with multiple labels and a suspected diagnosis of epilepsy, although there is considerable debate among

her support staff about this condition. Some strongly believe that she 'fakes' seizures (presumably for attention). In her new, less secure service, she frequently runs off. Initially, her support staff were told to follow her, but this often led to her swearing and shouting at them, knocking on people's doors and asking them to call the police. The strategy was changed after an analysis of the incidents, in which a number of themes emerged. First, Sandra appeared to have pretty good road sense, and the limited observations of her staff seemed to support this. Second, if she got lost, she would contact the service herself, which usually involved requesting a support person to pick her up. Third, an investigation into her past risky behaviours indicated that she had never been involved in any hospital admissions where she had been injured.'

Many strategies needed to be adopted in Sandra's case, but it was clear that there was an over-exaggeration of her actual behaviour. Running off led to understandably high levels of fear in her support staff. It was decided to obtain a mobile phone that she could use to call the service, and it was explained that when she ran off, she needed to tell them where she was or the police would have to be informed. Generally, she complied with this strategy. The use of mobile phones can be a positive intervention in many cases, such as the following:

'Anthony is a sixteen-year-old boy who has experienced many foster and residential care breakdowns. The final service he attended adopted low arousal principles. He would escape from the house using a number of sophisticated methods, one of which included obtaining a pin number for a security-coded lock. When he escaped, he would often meet up with some of the local adolescents and smoke cannabis. The service decided that, although his behaviours were

risky, they would give him a mobile phone and call him regularly to make sure he would return home. They also explained that they had a non-physical restraint policy, and that if he did not keep in regular contact, they would have to call the police. On a number of occasions, he would scream at staff, telling them to get out of his way - which they did. He would be offered his coat (especially as it was often quite cold) and given a fully charged mobile phone. Over time, the absconding rapidly decreased as his relationship with key staff improved. Nearly all of his past experiences involved the use of restraint. After his behaviour began to settle, he was formally interviewed by a young person's therapist who asked why he thought his behaviour had settled. He said, "They're not so bad here".'

With the advent of modern technology, some people may be tempted to resort to tracking systems. The use of tracking devices which are overtly placed on a person may have a place in situations of unplanned escape. However, there are real ethical issues with the covert tracking of people who have not committed any kind of offence. The use of the internet to monitor individuals also raises ethical concerns.

Strategic Capitulation

There are many situations in which a person can be literally and metaphorically fighting you. This book has given numerous examples of situations where people will continue to argue, in an almost ritualised manner. There are studies which demonstrate that many arguments and situations are repetitive in nature. Consider a common argument you have with someone you know well. Does that argument often feel repetitive? Even in care situations, escalations in behaviours of concern can appear to be highly ritualised. It is very difficult to change these scripts. Gary LaVigna and Todd Willis recommend that when a plan is not working, the best thing to do is to capitulate strategically. This means to stop resisting or fighting the individual. Giving in, for most individuals, is an extremely emotional process. Reconsider that everyday argument you have with a person close to you, and ask yourself the question, 'How important is it to win that argument?' This is more than a simple philosophical point. If a person's plan is not working and they are becoming extremely challenging on a routine basis, strategic capitulation means scrapping the plan. If a person needs to lie in bed all day in order to get through a crisis, then that should happen. The major problem with this approach is that it is a short-term solution, not a lifestyle. Think about a time in your life when you did not feel particularly positive; you may have been ill, emotionally distressed, or both. In these circumstances, you need time to rest and recuperate, rather than carry on regardless with the same plan or schedule.

Good Crisis Management Can Help Emotional Co-regulation

The concept of neuro-harmony emphasises creating a harmonious and synchronous environment (personal communication; Vermeulen, 2018). The transactional model of stress also emphasises that stress is interactional in nature. Focusing on the emotional and stress interactions between people can help towards achieving emotional regulation. In reality, it takes two people to create a harmonious, emotionally regulated state. When one individual is highly stressed, traumatised, and in a state of dysregulation, other individuals are forced to try and create a counterbalance to this. By remaining calm and adopting a low arousal approach, you are creating an opportunity for the distressed person to have time to self-regulate. Good crisis management involves good emotional co-regulation.

Achieving a greater sense of emotional regulation can depend on many different factors. Our brain development is linked to our emotional development. Young children do not learn to emotionally regulate by experience alone. They also have pre-programmed periods of time where their young brains are primed to develop these skills. Teaching a child to walk at three months is impossible, as the required muscles are insufficiently developed. Similarly, we are pre-programmed to understand the world, but we still require lived experiences to develop our own path. Learning how to express anger in an appropriate manner is a good example. We figure out the social rules as we get older, whilst, for some individuals, the ability to identify and manage their own emotions is a real problem. In some situations, a positive behaviour management intervention can lead to a person having the opportunity to reflect on their life:

'Mike is a thirty-eight-year-old ex-soldier who has a diagnosis of PTSD. Mike has a drug habit, which means that he is involved in street crime to meet his addiction needs. Mike has made it clear that he needs money to fuel his habit. He was lucky enough to be involved in a needle exchange and methadone programme. This enabled him to meet his needs, and led to him focusing on getting work and rebuilding his life.'

Creating a 'window of calmness' can lead to a period of reflection for individuals. Mike had a chance to get out of the vicious circle of fuelling his drug habit. Creating calm environments, from a low arousal perspective, may lead to opportunities for emotional and self-regulation. Remember, we must model regulation in order to help a person self-regulate. Therefore, we must appear ourselves to be emotionally regulated.

Property Destruction Can Encourage Self-Regulation

The most controversial advice about self-regulation is that, often when people damage property, they are actually attempting to achieve self-regulation. The following example illustrates this point:

'Lars is an adult with a mild intellectual disability and a history of anger control issues. Lars, for ten years, lived with two other people with similar issues to his own. For many years, he had achieved a state of equilibrium. There were very few episodes of physical aggression towards people, and life was pretty good. His staff team had changed over the years with people coming and going. There was a recent episode in which Lars became very angry with a new young member of staff, accusing her of touching his belongings. Lars actually became very aggressive and waved his fist at her. He then punched the wall in front of him and told her to leave. An emergency meeting was called to discuss Lars' frightening behaviour. At that meeting, it was noted that in the first three years of living with other people, Lars had been extremely violent on a number of occasions to staff. On one occasion, they even had to barricade themselves into an office until the police arrived to rescue them. It was agreed by all parties at the meeting that, whilst it was not desirable that Lars punch walls, based on his history he was actually making improvements by communicating to that member of staff that he wanted them to leave. It was pointed out by a very experienced person who had known him for years that, "In the past, he would have just hit you".'

Most people attempt some form of self-regulation. Some individuals may seek therapy, whilst for others, the passage of time is enough to achieve greater self-regulation, particularly over anger impulses. There is a need for people to understand that to self-regulate physical aggression, a person may need to compensate by increased verbal aggression, or even property destruction. This can only be understood by analysing a person's history. In my experience, we are creating situations where supporters are becoming increasingly intolerant of behaviours. Behaviours that seem quite bizarre or unusual may in fact be attempts to self-regulate. Here is an example:

'Amy is a twenty-one-year-old woman with a variety of labels (autism, OCD, and catatonia to name a few). Amy is supported by 2 to 1 staffing, 24 hours per day. Amy was moved to a new non-restraint service after being in a specialist service for 3 years, where there were at least 2 prone restraints per day, lasting an average of 9 minutes. As part of restraint decompression, staff were taught to withdraw from her line of sight and, if necessary, to use a Studio3 'walkaround' method (McDonnell, 2010). Over a 3-month period, physical restraint was nearly eradicated completely. The major area of concern for staff involved two forms of pulling hair. The first involved 'ritualised' hairpulling, where Amy would grab a member of staff's hair in a locking movement and attempt to lie on the ground. The second involved hairpulling where she would grab a person's hair and shake. Staff were taught methods to minimise injury. It was observed that both forms of hairpulling decreased. Interestingly, there were many recorded 'attempts at hairpulling', where Amy reached towards a member of staff, before appearing to stop and walk away. These were regarded as attempts at self-regulation. After one year, the hairpulling behaviours of all kinds had dramatically reduced. The 'attempts' also decreased, but at a much lower rate.

New rituals involving touching objects have increased, replacing the old hairpulling rituals.'

Amy appears to have had an 'automatic' component to her hairpulling. The previous service had used high levels of restraint, which in effect allowed her to calm down only if she was being held. In the new environment, she was given the space and time to self-regulate. The attempts at hairpulling are a good example of her battling to stop herself from engaging in the ritualised behaviour. Self-regulation is a key goal in any positive behaviour management approach. Property destruction, and even some forms of self-harm, may be attempts to avoid hurting other individuals. This may also be associated with the development of positive relationships. I once interviewed a young man with a borderline intellectual disability and severe epilepsy. Over a 9-year period, his behaviour had positively changed. I asked him, "In all this time that you have self-harmed, ran away and hurled abuse at people, why have you never hit one of your support staff?" His answer was simple; "I like them".

Allow Adequate Time for the Person to Calm Down

When supporting people who are highly distressed, knowing when to engage and when to retreat is a difficult skill to learn. The appropriate course of action will depend largely on your relationship with that person. We will sometimes over-engage a person in the hope that activities will help to distract them from their problems. The reality is that a person may need much more time to calm down than we often allow. Consider the following example:

'Quentin is a fifteen-year-old boy who struggles to regularly attend his local school. Quentin is described by his family as a quiet boy with a very intense and violent temper. Usually, he says sorry to his

parents after he has calmed down. It is clear that Quentin shows very little facial emotion in his day-to-day interactions with people. Quentin was described by his teacher as a 'grey man', a term they use to illustrate that it is hard to know what he is thinking and feeling. Quentin seemed to have many, consecutive, short-term incidents at home, which lasted between 3 to 5 minutes. These tended to occur in the evening, and often involved his irritation with his brothers and sisters. His parents often tried to re-engage with Quentin after an incident, telling him, "It's over" or "Try to stay calm". The advice the family received from a practitioner of the low arousal approach was to allow him more time to calm down and avoid interacting with him too much. They were advised to wait for his apology, and then ask him what was wrong. Over time, they reported fewer incidents.'

How do we judge that a person has calmed down enough to talk to? The best analogy is that of a car. When it travels really fast, the breaking distances massively increase. With children such as Quentin, it is sometimes difficult to judge when they have calmed sufficiently. It is often a good idea to reflect, on an individual basis, what a person's true indicators of calmness are. How long does this normally take? It is human nature to want to comfort a distressed individual. However, allowing a person to calm down may require patience and intuition. The theme of this book is that a low arousal approach is primarily about our own behaviour, and managing our own expectations.

Key Learning Questions

1) How important is eye contact, body language and physical proximity in conveying aggression and threat versus space and support?

2) What ten non-verbal strategies can be used to degrease demands when a person is distressed?

3) Name some ways that a person can learn to self-regulate their arousal levels. Consider which of these are seen as 'acceptable' and which are not, and why.

4) Think about ways that you can encourage people to 'back down' in crisis situations.

MANAGING THE POST-INCIDENT TURMOIL

Once the crisis appears to be over, the carer must allow time for recovery, which may take several hours. In some situations, this can take days. This period of recovery is not the time to ask for an apology, make any demands or reintroduce the initial trigger, as the individual will still be very aroused and may go straight back into another crisis. The emotional aftermath of a crisis can be difficult to understand and manage. Whilst there is considerable debate about the role of emotional support after stressful situations, in my opinion it is crucial to the well-being of individuals.

Supporting carers after exposure to incidents of aggression is an important aspect of the approach. Immediate debriefing (talking the incident through) may help carers to cope with the emotional aftermath of an incident. In addition, their thoughts and underlying belief structures may be altered as a consequence of their experiences. Therefore, an understanding of their perceptions and attributions is important.

Here are some simple guidelines for the debriefing process:

- Do it as soon after the incident as possible. This is an ideal scenario, as in many situations it can take days or weeks for a person to truly be emotionally ready to debrief and discuss an incident. In addition, people's recall of incidents can actively change over time. I remember when I was first trained, we were told that the first thing we should do after an incident is record it (typical of psychologists!). The reality is that the emotional component will have an impact on what we recall actually happened. There are numerous studies which show that people's recall can be inaccurate, and prone to prompting, even in cases where people have experienced violence (Lacy and Stark, 2013).

- Face to face is best, rather than speaking on the telephone. This should make it easier to judge how distressed the individual is. I should also point out that speaking to someone on the phone, although second-best, is still better than not speaking to someone at all.

- The person being debriefed must feel comfortable with the person they talk to, and trust them to keep the information confidential. If there is a mistake that people often make, it is to turn debriefing into some form of therapy. Debriefing is a form of emotional first aid - no more, no less.

- Trying to be non-judgemental can be extremely difficult. I learnt this the hard way when I managed a specialist community challenging behaviour team in Birmingham in the 1990s. I realised very quickly that my ability to emotionally debrief my colleagues was hampered by my managerial responsibilities. A simple example was that I could never promise people confidentiality, and on one occasion, I had to warn someone that what they were telling me would warrant further investigation. It is very clear that good debriefing from colleagues is open, honest, and allows the person to emotionally unburden in a non-judgemental way. This is not a time to offer solutions, but to actively listen to the person being debriefed.

- Often when people have calmed down, they will offer an apology to an individual who, in some circumstances, they may have actually assaulted. The low arousal approach would strongly advocate that accepting the apology is a more effective strategy than to refuse it (although the latter is perfectly understandable from an emotional perspective).

Reflecting on a violent situation is extremely important, especially if the incident is to be prevented in the future. Most people who support individuals with behaviours of concern have been involved in a situation where they have witnessed a person shouting, screaming, breaking property and sometimes even hitting people. I have found that the reflective questions you ask yourself after an incident are a really important factor in helping to 'move on'. I have developed the Post-Incident Reaction Plan (PIRP) to help with this process. Remember, the focus of this book is to reflect on your own attitudes towards people who display aggressive or challenging behaviour, rather than on the behaviour itself. When you experience a critical incident, you may find it useful to answer the following questions as honestly as you can as part of the debriefing process:

PIRP Post-Incident Reactive Plan			
	Yes	No	Action
Do you have a clear understanding of why the person behaved in the way they did?			
Do you still see the person as stressed and that impacting on their behaviour?			
Do you still see the person as traumatised and that impacting on their behaviour?			
Are you struggling to empathise with the person?			

Do you think the person's behaviour was planned and premeditated?			
Do you forgive the person?			
Are you angry with the person?			
Are you angry with your colleagues?			
Are you frightened of the individual?			
Are your colleagues frightened of the individual?			
Do you have a plan to help you re-engage with this person?			
Do you have a plan to prevent the incident from happening again?			
Have you learned anything about yourself due to the incident?			

When considering the wider aspects of emotional support, a minimum of four areas require a strong focus. These are; carers, other individuals connected to the individual (such as friends and family), the person themselves, and organisations. In all of these areas, a consistent emotional support plan needs to be in place in order to see significant changes in a person's emotional state.

Carers are often working in isolation, especially if they are family members of the person they support. These individuals should, where possible, have a trusted person that they can 'dump' their emotions on after challenging and emotional incidents. Sometimes this can be achieved by attending support groups or having a professional offer regular emotional check-ups. It is very important to avoid a sense of isolation in these circumstances. In contrast, we must also acknowledge that there are individuals who find it difficult to talk about their own feelings. In these situations, the type of support needed is often more practical in nature. Helping people with some of their chores or duties, or facilitating even the shortest of breaks, can help people to emotionally debrief and calm down after distressing incidents.

Other individuals who are connected to distressed people also require support, even if they have not directly witnessed a distressing situation. People can, in some cases, be vicariously traumatised by another person's distress. Sometimes people have very strong views that can be unhelpful:

'Vincent is a nineteen-year-old man who lives at home with his mother, and has a diagnosis of Asperger's Syndrome. Vincent often isolates himself when he is highly stressed, and struggles to

communicate face-to-face with his mother. A Studio3 practitioner suggested using texts instead of communicating in person. This appeared to increase his confidence in interacting with his mother. One year later, the same Studio3 practitioner was asked to respond to a crisis. They found that, as Vincent became less stressed, the extended family had placed a lot of pressure on his mother to discontinue this practice because it was 'not normal'. It was agreed to reinstate the texting method of communication, and Vincent's behaviour began to settle again.'

The distressed individual will sometimes be forgotten in the process of behaviour management. Often we can forget that, although they may appear angry, they can also be frightened and scared. If there is a common failing in a number of support organisations, it is that they do not allow distressed people sufficient non-judgemental emotional supports. People who are frequently aggressive will often view themselves as victims, even when they have physically harmed a person. Not allowing them to emotionally debrief from distressing incidents will only create future problems. However, it is difficult for people to be non-judgemental in these circumstances. The great humanist Carl Rogers always referred to the concept of unconditional positive regard for people as a key element in therapeutic engagement (Rogers, 1951). His is exactly the kind of emotional support that people require.

Sometimes, the staff group as well as the wider organisation may need a level of emotional containment. I remember a CEO of a disability organisation asking me quite forcefully, "Are my staff safe?" In order for a low arousal approach to be implemented across the board, there needs to be a good understanding by both floor staff and senior managers within the organisation. Here is a conversation that was held between a senior manager of a specialist behaviour support service and the CEO of an organisation after a person they supported had assaulted a member of the public and been arrested by the police:

CEO: Has this guy ever done anything like this before?

MANAGER: No

CEO: The press want me to make a statement, what should I say?

MANAGER: I think you should be honest and open, and say that we are supporting this individual to keep both him and the public safe, and that we are truly sorry somebody got hurt.

CEO: Are we clear on what happened?

MANAGER: Yes. He told the member of staff supporting him to 'get lost' and went to a pub. Our member of staff followed him and stayed in the background. He got into an argument with a guy at the bar and they started to struggle, until our member of staff got in between them and calmed things down. Unfortunately, the police had already been called, and when they arrived he became verbally aggressive towards them, and they arrested him.

CEO: OK, that's a little different to what I thought happened. Has he got a lawyer? Is anybody with him?

This real example highlights that sharing information is everything when systems begin to become stressed.

THE REFLECTIVE JOURNEY
Maintaining a Positive Relationship With the Distressed Individual

A low arousal approach means adopting a person-centred approach to crisis management. In care environments when a carer is confronted with aggression, a low arousal approach suggests that the carer may be expected to show a high degree of tolerance. Maintaining a positive relationship with distressed individuals may therefore prove difficult for carers, particularly if their behaviours are particularly aggressive or challenging. Acknowledging the distress a carer feels is sometimes enough to help them tolerate distressed behaviour. In my experience, you should always avoid phrases such as 'I understand' when talking to other carers about a distressing experience they have had. The simple reason for this is that you can never truly experience the same emotions as that individual, and they may find it to be dismissive of their lived experience. A useful strategy to consider when people become more negative about an individual they support is to encourage them to think of the more positive interactions that have had with that person. It is far more difficult to isolate yourself emotionally from a person with whom you have developed a strong bond after a challenging incident has occurred. In these circumstances, you may feel more aggrieved and hurt that a person you support has behaved in a certain manner towards you. This emotional connection is key to supporting people, and therefore it is incredibly important to cultivate good, positive relationships with individuals in your care.

Think about how difficult it is to meet up with a friend or a colleague after you have had some form of intense disagreement. What do you say? Who starts the conversation? Do you tell the person to forget the argument? Many people who support distressed people often struggle to re-engage with that person after an incident. They are conflicted between their fear of harm and their desire to help that person. There are often situations where people will simply refuse to re-engage with  a person who physically or emotionally harmed them.

There are two simple re-engagement strategies that I would recommend. The first is very much behavioural, and involves not discussing what happened until the distressed person brings up the subject. The second approach is more engaging. It involves acknowledging that something happened, and that there is a need to 'move on'.

Developing Organisational Responses

Managing crises in a low arousal approach does not in itself change the behaviour. However, it can help to de-escalate crisis situations, and pave the way for a calmer, more regulated life for a distressed individual. In terms of intellectual disability services, creating organisations which encourage staff to adopt low arousal strategies is an area that has received less emphasis. Likewise, in family settings, the low arousal approach needs to be a way of life encouraged and adopted by the whole family; it is not just for dealing with a crisis. The altering of environmental factors which reduce physiological arousal is an important facet of the approach, and something that should be implemented in schools and services where arousal can be easily impacted by other people, noise and other sensory stimuli. Individuals with autism spectrum disorders (ASD) who exhibit behaviours of concern may often be subject to lots of rules and boundaries, an overuse of which can actually increase the likelihood of conflict rather than reduce it. Therefore, low arousal strategies can involve the reduction of general rules and boundaries. Although such approaches can be challenging for staff and carers, empowering individuals to make their own choices can lead to reductions in behaviours of concern and increased well-being (Pitonyak, 2005).

Key Learning Questions

1) What do you understand by the term 'debriefing'?

2) What are the best strategies for getting a colleague or friend to talk about their emotional experiences?

3) What forms of emotional support work best for you?

4) When you have witnessed a distressing situation, who do you talk to about it in your own life?

PART THREE: CONTINUING THE JOURNEY

CHAPTER 13

FIGHTING OUR INNER DEMONS

This book is called *The Reflective Journey* for a very good reason, being that managing the difficult behaviours of other people is in fact much more about managing our own responses to distressed situations. A good low arousal intervention plan may, at times, require non-intervention. This can be extremely difficult for people to carry out in practice. A major criticism of the approach is that people sometimes feel that they have had to 'give in' to an individual's demands.

This 'win or lose' mindset can be extremely unhelpful in day-to-day practice. Feelings of helplessness can be difficult to understand, but it is important to acknowledge that sometimes in our work, we may feel helpless. Fighting our inner 'demons' is an essential part of this journey, and this includes challenging our own beliefs about what it means to manage behaviour. Think of a situation you have experienced where you prevented yourself from saying something nasty to a person. Did you have negative thoughts and emotional reactions after the situation occurred? Low arousal approaches can lead to situations where conflict has been successfully avoided. However, when people resist the urge to 'fight', they are to a certain degree left in 'emotional limbo'. In the Deep South of the US, civil rights supporters used non-violence as a strategy in protests. Mahatma Gandhi used similar tactics to help India gain independence from Britain. It is easy to admire people who choose a non-violent path, but to follow such a path requires incredible self-control. To quote a colleague, 'restraining someone is relatively easy; not restraining someone takes courage'. In this chapter, we will examine some of the challenges to applying the low arousal approach in everyday situations.

Low Arousal Approaches Can Be Counter-Intuitive

When we are supporting a distressed person, we try to focus on managing behaviours, but naturally we also bring into this melting pot our own personality and beliefs. If some of the ideas in this book appear counter-intuitive, you may feel challenged to question your own approach. Where does it stem from? What moments in your past or in your career have turned you into the practitioner you are today? Sometimes our instinct is to react to situations, and quite often we can use commands like 'Stop doing that', or 'No, I want you to do this'. Resisting the urge to say things in the moment can appear to be the opposite of what most people in society would do. Sometimes, to distract a person who is highly aroused and upset, we may use tangible things such as food or drink; for example, offering to make someone a cup of tea. In my experience, many people start to see this as potentially rewarding bad behaviour. We do have deeply held beliefs about managing behaviours, and as low arousal practitioners we are constantly fighting our urge to respond. Most arguments or disputes will end with some form of negotiation, and that often involves compromise. Negotiating with a distressed person may appear to many people as 'backing down'. In my experience, much of the advice I gave to families or individuals about managing crises was too prescriptive in the past. To give a good example of this, I used to tell people to avoid giving people attention or reinforcing bad behaviour. In the present day, my experiences tell me to no longer advise this. Many of the things I was taught as a professional psychologist were very helpful. However, I now realise how over-simplistic some of my advice was as a young practitioner. It is very clear that what is best for managing crises in the moment is different from our beliefs and ideas about changing and altering behaviours.

Fighting Your Instincts

Much has been made of the concept of fight, flight or freeze. Much of the guidance in this book requires you to, to a certain degree, fight these instincts. Confrontation is to be avoided at all costs when using a low arousal approach. At some point in our careers, we may have ended up using our 'fight' response in terms of having verbal arguments and, in extreme cases, the use of physical restraint. 'Flight' is only an option in limited circumstances. If we are responsible for a young child who is extremely distressed, we cannot simply run away (no matter how we feel). Parents of distressed children and young people also do not have the luxury of running away. However, we nearly always have an option to withdraw. In military terminology, tactically withdrawing from an impossible situation is often the best approach. As the phrase goes, 'He who fights and runs away, lives to fight another day'. The ancient philosopher Sun Tzu, in his book *The Art of War,* argues that knowing when to fight and when to withdraw is crucial to success (5th Century BC). However, resisting the urge to 'stand your ground' is a very difficult process.

One way to achieve this is to be more focused 'in the moment'. In my opinion, this can be developed like any other skill. Mindfulness-based approaches have the concept of being aware and present at their core. Focusing on the 'here and now' is not any easy process. Here is a good example:

'Sheila is sixty-eight years of age. She has a twin sister called Alice. For 10 years, Sheila has been Alice's main supporter, as she suffered a stroke resulting in brain injury. Alice has rapid changes in mood which can result in verbal rages. She has at times broken objects and, although rarely, she has hit Sheila on several occasions. Sheila has become an expert at managing her sister's explosive temper. She has developed strategies which allow her to 'tune in' and 'tune out' when her sister is very agitated. Her strategies include a great deal of positive self-motivation, reminding herself not to take what her sister says to her to heart. In addition, she allows her sister time to calm down. Nonetheless, there are times when she needs to walk away from her sister and regroup herself.'

Sheila sees her sister as a person who is changing and needs her help. Her respect and love for her sister allow her to see the person and not the distressed behaviour. Sheila's ability to remove herself mentally and physically from difficult situations allows her to avoid confrontation with her sister, and thus better support her.

Low arousal approaches can create and expose deep emotional conflicts in people. The concept of cognitive dissonance is very relevant to this approach. When a person holds two or more contradictory beliefs, they try to resolve these differences by a process known originally as cognitive dissonance (Festinger, 1957). People instinctively try to resolve differences in a number of ways. Most importantly, they may resolve to support only one point of view, or minimise their view of a situation. People may also attempt to rationalise their positions and beliefs. For example, a heavy smoker who over-eats may rationalise that they are not very unhealthy because they also regularly train in the gym.

Dissonance is very relevant when practitioners apply the low arousal approach. Consider the following example:

'Aimee is a parent with two young children. One of her children has a number of challenges and he requires much more of her time than his older brother. Aimee feels guilty that one of her sons gets more attention, and her other son has told her that she is being unfair. Aimee strongly believes that she should treat her two children equally, but she knows that this is not practical.'

How can Aimee resolve these two issues? The simple answer is that she cannot in the short-term. She has to accept that, at the present time, she cannot be as fair as she would like to be. She must resolve the difference by accepting the situation. When applying the low arousal approach, we may inadvertently create deep emotional conflicts. Jo Billington, an autism researcher and parent, expressed to me in an interview that for her, low arousal a created deep conflict as many of the ideas appeared to be counter-intuitive (personal communication, 2019). Sometimes it looks as though we are advising people to 'back down' or 'give in'. This creates dissonance as most parents believe that their role is to guide their children rather than leave them to find their own way. The reality is that we *can* guide our children and the people we support, but when a person is 'melting down', that is not the best time to be teaching them rules. Parents, like all other people, should 'pick their moments' when giving guidance.

Similar issues exist when working with adults. It can be difficult not to impose rules on individuals, but a low arousal approach simply means reducing the number of rules individuals have, not eradicating rules altogether. We are sometimes guilty of treating adults as though they are young children. Their behaviour, which can be viewed as childlike, creates a deep sense of conflict in us. The therapist Eric Berne, in his book *Games People Play,* highlighted this point many years ago (1964). Berne proposed that all of our human interactions are guided by deeply-learned ego states, such as parent, adult and child states. Berne's proposed that there are a number ego states we switch between when interacting with people. He referred to these different roles as being part of a 'game', but it is easier to think of them as overread scripts that we feel compelled to act out. Applying this theory to adults interacting with other adults who appear to be acting in a 'childlike' manner, there is one ego mode that is particularly relevant – the 'critical parent'. Critical parent behaviours generally act out the corrective behaviours of real parents and the prohibitive messages of society. The more we perceive someone as misbehaving, the more critical we become. In my experience, most people - particularly parents - do not like to view themselves as being critical of behaviour. However, this is a mode that we can easily slip into, almost without being aware that we are doing it:

'Ludmilla is an adult with a borderline intellectual disability who often displays what her support staff call childlike behaviours and 'temper tantrums' (a phrase that should be avoided). *She swears and laughs at her support staff and sometimes, when she is really stressed, she smears faeces on the walls of her bedroom or urinates in the corner of her room. Her support staff agreed on a plan where she was gently and consistently prompted to clear her mess up. Their reason for this was that she has to learn 'appropriate behaviours'. It was very clear that many staff did not do this in a gentle manner.'*

This example illustrates that, sometimes, the nature of the behaviour can evoke a powerful emotional response. The staff's 'behaviour plan' was at best archaic. Consider why the staff may have felt that the most important thing in this situation was for her to clean her mess up. If a child is unwell and vomits, would you make them clean it up? How is this situation any different? A more effective plan would have been to figure out what is causing her stress and how to relieve it. A simple low arousal strategy would involve a calm and supportive response, as opposed to concentrating on imposing consequences and attempting to correct behaviour. In this situation, the plan made by staff clearly has elements of the critical parent. The following statements attempt to express what the staff may have been thinking in this situation, and expose the underlying emotional conflict that led to their actions.

Ludmilla is doing this to annoy us and is seeking attention.

Ludmilla needs to learn that we will not tolerate this behaviour.

Ludmilla needs to be taught a lesson.

If I did this in my house, my parents would have done the same.

People are often unaware that they think in this way. It is easy to see why people may believe that they are teaching people the appropriate way to behave. In this case, Ludmilla's behaviours were perceived as being wilful and deliberate, and her supporters saw her as a misbehaving child who had to learn appropriate behaviour. It is fascinating how easily we slip into this mode of thinking. A positive script would read more like this:

Ludmilla is highly stressed at the moment.

I do not like the mess she creates; it is unpleasant.

I will not make a big deal about it.

I will not treat her like a child.

I need to figure out what is causing her stress levels to be so high.

There are many deep-rooted emotional scripts that we learn almost unconsciously from an early age. The low arousal approach can dislodge some of these deep-seated conflicts, and cause us to challenge our own beliefs. This is why it is so important that anyone adopting these strategies must be ready and willing to explore their own thoughts, feelings and emotions. It is incredibly challenging to turn the lens on ourselves when we have been conditioned to analyse and examine the person with behaviours of concern. Low arousal is not the easy option in Ludmilla's case, or in any case for that matter. The easy option is to focus on her behaviours as things that need to be changed, rather than acknowledge that perhaps we are the ones who need to change.

THE REFLECTIVE JOURNEY
Fighting the 'Tough Love' Mantra

The idea that we have to be 'cruel to be kind' has been partly attributed to the German philosopher Fredriche Neitsche. The Nazis often cited his work as justification that to develop as 'supermen', people have to be strong. Neitsche's many famous quotations have often been misinterpreted over the years. The fascinating truth is that this gentle philosopher and intellectual was not quite the tough person that the world believed. It is alleged that he never recovered fully from witnessing a horse being cruelly beaten as a young man, and certainly did not gain in strength from the experience.

The 'tough love' mantra is in some way fuelled by a society who wants to believe that punishment works. We watch Supernanny on television and admire the heroine who arrives at a home that is in disarray, managing to restore order after some reflection and tactical use of the 'naughty step'. There are so many strong cultural influences about 'good' parenting and being firm. In ancient Sparta, citizens were encouraged to beat young warriors if they showed any fear or weakness. It is true that the Spartans produced fearsome warriors, though, I fear, unhappy ones. In the US, Boot Camps for young offenders have a strong emphasis on correcting difficult or unsociable behaviour. It is interesting to note that the US has one of the highest prison populations in the world (Walmsley, 2018). The following real-life example shows quite clearly how power imbalances, combined with the 'tough love' mantra, can have a negative impact:

'Jessica is a twelve-year-old girl who lives with her foster parents. Her behaviour has become more and more reckless over the years. She is described as 'defiant' by her foster family, and is known to

find rules very difficult to follow. Her foster family decided to 'crack down' on her, feeling that in order to avoid her behaviour deteriorating further, they needed to 'come down hard on her'. They adopted a rule-based 'tough love' programme and began training in physical restraint. The programme involved Jessica having to earn points to receive 'privileges'. Her television and access to the internet were removed, and even books were restricted. Acts of defiance were met with restraint (described as 'gentle holding') until Jessica complied. Her foster parents sincerely believed that this was the best course of action. They noted that, in the first six weeks, Jessica was being more compliant and less defiant. Jessica, on the other hand, describes this period of her life as 'absolute hell'. The programme was halted very rapidly once Studio3 became involved.'

It is easy to read this example and assume that the foster parents were simply cruel and inhumane. In reality, they were seduced by the 'tough love' mantra. Things had become so desperate that such a programme was viewed as being worth a try. Many people reading this book will know that adolescence is a difficult time for children and adults alike. Making young people comply often builds up emotional resentment between carer and child. In the autism field, the debate about whether autism can be 'cured' by behavioural intervention has been extremely controversial. I once had a conversation with a leading educationalist about claims that the early intervention approach, developed by Lovaas in the US, could 'cure' autism (1987). My view was very simple: you can make a person behave in a particular way by using punishment-based interventions, but it does not change their way of being. To quote Janusz Korczak, 'Whatever has been achieved through pressure and violence is unstable, unreliable and incorrect' (1929).

Tough parenting debates can be linked to the varied societal views of corporal punishment. I myself was of the generation in the 1970s where UK school punishments varied from a 'light tap' on the backside to a cane across either the backside or hands. To this very day, the resulting resentment of teacher authority is still strong. It would have been wonderful if the teacher who championed this approach had read the work of humanists like Janusz Korczak. There is little doubt that they truly believed that such punishments maintained levels of discipline across the school and increased good behaviour. In reality, when the cane and other forms of corporal punishment were abolished in UK schools, there was little impact on the behaviour of pupils (Morrison, 2014).

Changing Our Own Beliefs and Attitudes

Can we change attitudes and deep-seated beliefs? My colleague, the late Michael McCreadie, and I had an in-depth debate about whether beliefs and attitudes can ever be altered or fundamentally changed. Is your personality fixed from a young age, or is it possible to change your views? The answer is uncertain in either case. However, I believe that people can change under the right circumstances. It is difficult for people to challenge social rules and norms, but it is certainly possible. Consider the following example of Adrian, a nurse working in an institutional setting for people with intellectual disabilities:

'Adrian works on a locked ward for adults with very complex needs. The ward is also an admissions area for people in behavioural crises. Adrian has worked there for over 12 years, and, over the years, has imposed many rules and boundaries. He believed in the past that being 'firm' with people was the correct approach. He admitted that

he often did not challenge practices that his colleagues believed were 'normal'. Adrian began a gradual change process, through which he started to believe that if the low arousal approach was correct, some of the practices he had participated in had been wrong. He had imposed too many rules and supported the 'Status Quo'. He began to change his approach and started to relax rules when his colleagues were not working. Most importantly, he allowed people to express their anger and avoided the use of restraint and the sanctions that usually followed. Adrian became a passionate advocate for the low arousal approach, eventually becoming a manager and leading by example.'

In my experience, it is difficult to judge who can change their deep-rooted beliefs. Adrian was not somebody who gave any indication that he supported the low arousal approach, yet he was extremely motivated to change. In this book we have mentioned a great deal about changing our focus from viewing people as the enemy in battle, to seeing distressed people who need our help. Psychologist Howard Gardner, in his book *Changing Minds,* argues that there are many different ways to change our thinking (2004). It is rare that a deeply-held belief or attitude changes with one single event - although it is possible. Logic and traumatic learning are pathways, but the most important is 'gut feeling', or resonance as Gardner calls it. Over the last 30 years, my colleagues and I have worked to try to eradicate physical restraint from care environments. This is a huge goal, and to some it may sound impossible, but we can achieve this by showing people that change is possible.

Control Versus Responsibility

My colleague Bo Heilskov Elvén is currently studying the application of low arousal approaches to family settings as part of his doctoral work at Birmingham City University. Bo argues that people often confuse care and responsibility in their application of low arousal approaches. We sometimes have to consider the ethical questions that apply when intervening in certain situations. In hospital situations, doctors may carry out necessary procedures in a crisis when they do not have consent. Their primary focus in these situations is the safety of the person. In some circumstances, we may need to take control of the situation in order to ensure the safety of everyone involved. However, there can be times where we may take control of a risky situation when it is not justified. It is important to consider a person's ability to make informed and rational decisions in a crisis, as this process may be compromised if the person is highly distressed. Consider this example:

'Sam is a forty-two-year-old man with high functioning autism, who lives in his own flat with daily supports. Although he likes his support staff, he will sometimes shout and swear at them when he is angry or upset, and tell them to leave. On a number of occasions, he has 'fired' them. In the past, support organisations took him at his word and withdrew staff, leaving him even more distressed and unsupported. A new organisation was put in place to support him, and it was made clear to Sam that firing his staff required measured steps as they needed to be responsible employers'.

In the above example, many people abandoned Sam, saying that he 'had made his choice'. However, to walk away and take him at his word fails to take into account the fact that he was extremely distressed, and not in control of his actions. This withdrawal of support was unethical, especially as it inevitably led to even more distress from Sam. Even within a low arousal approach, there should be a balance between freedom and control. The simple mantra for practitioners should be that 'highly stressed people make poor decisions'. Creating a balance between the person's freedom to choose and what is in their best interests requires a process of constant evaluation and re-evaluation. In sum, when adopting a low arousal approach, simply withdrawing from people as a long-term strategy is a misinterpretation of your role as a supporter. Our role is still to assist people, and this sometimes means that the more stressed someone becomes, the more simplistic our forms of communication must be. In reality, we may sometimes appear to be taking control of a situation in crisis, but this should only ever be a short-term, temporary strategy.

Catastrophic Thinking

Aron T. Beck, one of the leading experts on cognitive behavioural therapy (CBT), highlighted a number of cognitive (thinking) processes that we all have hard wired into our brains (1976). We will often catastrophise about situations, creating a sense of hopelessness and fear. In our work, this type of thinking can quickly create a mindset of fear and a culture of risk avoidance. Before I was a qualified clinical psychologist, I worked in an institution for people with intellectual disabilities and mental health issues where there was a strong culture of fear amongst staff. I was asked to work on the 'locked ward' in order to get a sense of what it was like to work there. There, I was inducted by a young manager who told me the following:

"You need to be very vigilant when working here, as we work with some really difficult and violent people. In fact, I have been telling management that we need more staff, or else someone is going to get seriously injured, or even killed."

After this terrifying induction, I entered the locked ward to find that the general atmosphere was one of boredom and inactivity. The 'patients' (as they were referred to by the dehumanising language of the 80s) were frightened and traumatised people. After the initial fear and uncertainty, there was no sign of the unsafe culture described by the manager. Today, it is clear to me that this is a classic example of staff 'catastrophising' a handful of incidents into a larger, pervasive problem. A similar process can involve magnifying an emotional incident or situation until becomes a story of almost legendary proportions. In the 1980s, I attended a managing violence workshop where the lead trainer spent a great deal of time talking about the most scary incidents he had ever encountered. He appeared to be a great storyteller (with a huge ego), and all it seemed to achieve was to scare new staff and give them the impression that they had taken on a job in a war zone. It is really easy in these circumstances for individuals with behaviours of concern to become demonised, their reputations growing as stories are elaborated with each retelling, to the point where fiction and reality diverge. It is important to stress that a small minority of supporters can become 'negative messengers', almost delighting in transferring negative messages about people. I often use the German phrase 'Schadenfreude', which means to take pleasure in the suffering of others, to explain this mechanism.

High levels of fear and catastrophising can be a dangerous cocktail, leading to excessive use of restraint and other restrictive practices. The restraint reduction rhetoric is often different from the practice. In theory, we use physical restraint as a last resort, but in reality, it can often be the first resort (McDonnell and Deveau, 2009). Restraint and its application can be highly addictive in nature. When it is used once, we begin a psychological process of justifying the action. The concept of cognitive dissonance is also a useful idea to think about in this context. We may have very positive values and describe ourselves as person-centred practitioners, but if we accept these values and at the same time use physical restraint, we create dissonance within ourselves. That is, both beliefs become unstable due to the presence of the other. This dissonance is sometimes resolved by an over-justification of why restraint (or seclusion) had to be applied in specific occasions. Common justifications include the following:

'To keep people safe'

'To protect property'

'To prevent self-harm'

'To stop a behaviour escalating further'

Many of these reasons may well be valid 'in the moment'. However, if we start to believe that we have exhausted all options then we will never change our own practice. People can begin to see restraint as almost an acceptable side effect of their work - a necessary evil. We are also aware that groups of individuals can be subject to the phenomenon of groupthink. Groupthink occurs when a group of people agree on an irrational or illogical point, simply due to a desire for harmony within the group (Tajfel, 1979). This most often occurs when powerful people justify their positions and prevent other people from having their say. The lack of autonomy within the group allows each member to somehow justify the actions of the group as a separate entity.

However, it is not helpful to be negative in our view. Time and time again, we have stressed that people can change:

'A young man named Andrew once worked as part of a support staff for people with disabilities many years ago. He was trained in a specific one-person restraint hold, which involved sitting an individual in a chair and holding their hands together. He was then expected to place his knee and full bodyweight across the person's lap to help immobilise them. The first time he had to do this, he felt positive that it had 'worked'. However, after the second time, he started to feel uneasy about what he was doing. He justified it by saying to himself, 'well, there is no other way to do this'. The other justification was that he did not have to do it very often. It took several months for him to realise that walking out of the room or walking into an open space was just as effective.'

The person in this example shares my name because we are one and the same. As a twenty-two-year-old, optimistic support worker, I started by doing what I was told. A year after this, I worked in an institutional setting and witnessed the use of a variety of prone and supine holds, as well as the use of seclusion. It took nearly a full year after this for me to realise that the vast majority of these restraints were not only unnecessary but actually traumatising, for the person being restrained as well as for staff. This led to the birth of Studio3 in 1992. At the time, it was quite a radical step to avoid using certain types of restraint. I often wonder why it took nearly 8 years for me to come to the conclusion that so many restraints were unnecessary. I believe that many people genuinely think there is no choice but to use these methods. The consequence of this is that every example of restraint avoidance and applying low arousal approaches to this day evokes mixed emotions in me. The first emotion is always a positive justification that alternatives can be effective when people are given a chance to use them. The second is both guilt and shame, usually surrounding my own past applications of restraint. The most common thought is always, 'Why did I not challenge these practices enough when I was younger?'

We must also acknowledge that there are countless examples of small groups of highly influential people who rationalise and justify these practices, as well as a relatively small minority who actually seem to enjoy the exhilaration and excitement of restraining or secluding distressed individuals. This doesn't mean that everyone who has used restraint methods is inherently bad. However, an examination of the many famous abuse inquiries leads to a consistent theme; that cultures of restraint and other restrictive practices become almost normalised and justified by people. In sum, power can be abused by people, and that is why regulatory monitoring of care situations and support of people in their own homes is a necessity.

People can begin to change their practices when they are truly honest about them. The following example of institutional practice demonstrates how, with enough reflection and experimentation, people can change:

'Happy Acres is a hospital setting that caters for a wide range of individuals, including people with intellectual disabilities, autism, older adults and a wide range of other psychiatric labels. The hospital is not particularly highly staffed, and the levels of activity are particularly poor. There is a real division between newer staff (who often want to change things) and older staff, who quite often give the message that this is 'a really dangerous place'. Eventually, many newer staff, through a process of time and groupthink, began to mimic the behaviours of their colleagues. However, there were a hardcore group of people who wanted change. Happy Acres was quite well known, as it had been the subject of a national investigation where it was publicly damned for dehumanising practices. The team brought in to help to implement changes were highly experienced practitioners, though they were at first overwhelmed by the enormity of the task. They began by working with staff in regards to the individuals who attracted the highest levels of restrictions. They trained staff in low arousal approaches, and soon found that some of the training was highly emotive and challenging as many staff did not see why they could not seclude or hold people down on the ground. Over a three year process, more and more staff were won over to the approach, and restraints were reduced by nearly 90% amongst targeted individuals.'

Did the world fundamentally change? Did the individuals have increased levels of meaningful activity? The honest answer is 'no'. Were the individuals safer? Did it encourage change by the reduction of restrictive practices? The answer to these questions is a resounding 'yes'. This example shows that we can make small but meaningful changes in highly institutionalised places. The key is demonstrating best practice and teaching alternative methods. This process also requires people with proverbial 'thick skin' and a high level of passion and determination. My view is that, unless people experiment with alternatives to restraint, nothing changes. In addition, getting the basics right will encourage a change process in which people can dare to dream that change is really possible. In these extreme situations, change occurs when practices are challenged and there is a 'bottom up' approach, whereby practitioners lead by example. The concept of emotional contagion, referred to in earlier chapters, also applies to positive emotions of hope and optimism. By modelling confidence using non-aversive behaviour management strategies, we can influence change in our colleagues, and positively impact the lives of the people we support.

Fear (as discussed in Chapter Five) can be a powerful motivator for people justifying extreme responses to distressed behaviours. There are some situations in which trying to understand a process is very necessary. The following real-life example highlights this point perfectly:

'Jamal and Shazia are a working class couple with a twelve-year-old son with autism and severe intellectual disabilities. Their son, Mahmood, could be extremely physically aggressive towards his two younger siblings. He had bitten his little sister on one occasion where she had required hospital admission. The family sought little external help as they believed that they should cope with this situation alone, and were ashamed to admit that they were not in control. When their son's behaviour was more distressed, he would try to escape by jumping out of the first floor window of their home, smear himself in faeces and, most commonly, when his parents held him he would kick, bite and scratch them. In desperation, his father converted the cupboard under the stairs into what he described as 'safe area'. It was small, bare, and covered in matted cushions to stop their son

banging his head. The entrance was a converted iron gate that could be padlocked. At night, he was locked into his bedroom with secure windows. The parents' justification was that they could see and talk to their son, whilst keeping the family safe. They were horrified and shocked when a neighbour reported them for child abuse. After a brief investigation, the young boy was removed from their care and never fully returned to the family home.'

This example shows that stressed people may justify extreme strategies to keep people safe. I have always thought that we must keep people safe and protect them. However, we should also acknowledge that providing people with training and strategies to manage these situations would be a more effective approach. The is no doubt that we must always challenge our own inner demons, and resist the urge to use procedures such as restraint and seclusion. There are always alternatives in my opinion.

Key Learning Questions

1) Can you think of a situation or experience in which your thinking became catastrophic? If this was in response to fear or uncertainty, how could you manage these thoughts in the future?

2) What is 'groupthink'? How can it be avoided?

3) We all have our own 'inner demons' when it comes to working in particular situations with particular individuals. Try to identify some of your own. Acknowledging our

difficulties in certain areas can help us to overcome these fears and become more confident practitioners.

4) Why is it important to reduce levels of restraint?

CHAPTER 14

BEYOND CRISIS MANAGEMENT

The goal of this book is to assist the reader to enhance and further develop their skills using a 'reflective approach'. It must be remembered that a reflective approach which is truly inward-looking is always going to be a difficult process. We exist in a social world where we constantly relate to and interact with people. Understanding these interactions, and in effect our own contribution to behavioural situations, is the core idea of this book. By definition, our own life experiences have a great influence on our approach to managing crises. By completing the exercises in this book, you have chosen to continue your personal journey. This is a slow and dynamic process that will continue to evolve as we get older. Think about how your own attitudes have changed and evolved over the course of your life. Think about some of the viewpoints that you have strongly held that may have changed with time, experience and, of course, reflection. Much of this book has been about crisis management. In this last section, let us think about going beyond crisis management.

Inevitably, a focus on low arousal approaches to crisis management will lead the reader to a perspective about how behaviours can be altered or changed. Remember, good crisis management will allow us to develop and grow a positive relationship between ourselves and the people we support, hopefully creating a 'space' for reflection. This 'space' will always create an opportunity to focus on a more meaningful and long-term positive approach. For the last part of this book, let us consider the low arousal approach and how it can influence our perspective on changing behaviours.

Low Arousal Does Not Mean No Arousal!

If there is a major myth about the low arousal approach, it is the idea that people are expected to 'give in' and do nothing with the people they support. The reality is that we are trying to create a period of low-stress and calmness in which engaging with a distressed person is the priority. Low arousal means, quite simply, lowering levels of arousal. There should always be a strong focus on positive interaction, even in the most difficult circumstances. Take the following as an example:

*'Colin is a twenty-four-year-old boy with an abusive history. He also has severe learning disabilities and profound communication problems. He has no spoken language and a limited vocabulary of words he understands. Colin resists attempts to engage in activities that are thought to be meaningful (*which, arguably, they are not*). Colin attends a specialist day service where he receives one-to-one*

half hour teaching sessions throughout a full and busy day. Staff record, using a stopwatch, the amount of time he spends chasing them and being aggressive. His average is approximately twenty minutes per session. His key worker decided to scrap all of his so-called 'engagement' programmes. Without calling it a low arousal approach, the goal changed to sitting with him quietly, no closer than two metres apart, in a soft play area. His key worker chose to systematically sit closer to Colin over a four-week period. Activities were changed to eating small snacks and listening to nursery rhymes, with a focus on creating a positive relationship. After a three-month period, his key worker was able to sit very close to Colin and get him to engage with simple, meaningful tasks.'

This early attempt, which we would now most certainly describe as a low arousal approach, also had a positive engagement goal. The idea of scrapping all his activity programmes and starting again was not an easy task. Reducing demands and requests does not mean that we create a situation of anarchy. We all require some basic rules and structure to exist with other people. Therefore, reducing rules in a low arousal approach is not the same as having no rules at all.

Manage Your Own Stress First

It is critical we understand that stress management starts with ourselves. There are many examples of stressful occupations that have associated high risks of ill health or harm. Air traffic controllers, who have a highly stressful occupation, can present with relatively high rates of mental health issues. One area also relevant to the low arousal approach is home carers. Often, people are caring for individuals with relatively little support. In the UK, it is thought that

700,000 people care for over 850,000 people with a diagnosis of Dementia (Lewis et al, 2014).

We need to be good positive role models for stress management. Looking after your own stress is therefore critical as we need to be able to support others (Woodcock and Page, 2010). David Pitonyak focuses a great deal on what he describes as 'supports for the supporters' (2005). There are many analogies to describe this position. To share water from a well there needs to be a good healthy constant supply of fresh clear water. If you allow your own well to run dry then there is nothing left for other people. It is surprising that people who support highly distressed individuals are often quite poor at managing their own emotional self-care. Many people, when confronted with situations where they are expected to cope with high demands, forget that they are not superhuman.

In the children's field, open and honest role models are a crucial part of creating a culture of well-being and positive mental health (Knightsmith, 2018). This does not mean that supporters must constantly talk about these issues. Rather, that modelling a reflective and open approach allows people to make useful distinctions. Consider the connotations of declaring that you feel 'burnt out'. I once encountered a now eminent psychologist who stated that 'burn-out is a zero-sum game'. What does this mean? The answer is simple; if you ask yourself the question, 'How burnt out am I?', the score will eventually get higher. The opposite of stress and burnout is resilience. Focusing on your resilience levels makes it possible to cope with a wide range of stressors, and is a key factor in the positive coping strategies discussed earlier in this book.

Slow Down: Changing Behaviour Takes Time

If there is a recurring theme in this book, it is that we should accept that many behaviours are complex in nature, and multiply determined. Accepting complexity does not mean that we are helpless to do anything, but it does mean that true changes in behaviour may take a considerable amount of time. I have often found that the families and staff teams that I work with set goals over weeks and months, whereas I set goals over months and years. With both children and adults, there is often a desire to change a person's behaviour. Educational settings are good examples of this. Good schools encourage learning by creating environments to support this. However, there is always an underlying message that children will need to pass examinations. A school is a place of learning, and therefore it is true that a school could be considered derelict in its duty if it stated that examinations were not a goal. However, there should be a recognition that student learning styles differ, and that young people learn at different rates. Many parents worry about their children's educational attainment, even when the evidence suggests that their child is thriving and flourishing.

Sometimes approaches can be too driven to achieve rapid results, with disastrous consequences. In the autism field, the heated debates about the effectiveness of early intervention programmes, such as applied behaviour analysis (ABA), have been steeped in controversy. I am reminded of a teacher in a school for individuals with autism who used a low arousal approach to ABA. She summarised it very succinctly by saying, "I use many of the behavioural techniques, but I always carry out a programme depending on the learning pattern of the child". Teachers often set a blistering pace which can increase stress for some individuals. I find that a slow pace in a low arousal environment helps all pupils, not only those with additional needs. Most importantly, if a child is very stressed or really struggling with a programme, I will give them lots of breaks or even the day off from the programme. Remember, learning is supposed to be fun. This example shows that we do not have to 'throw the baby out with the bath water'; we just need to appreciate that programmes need to be individualised. This does not just apply to schools and other educational settings. There will always be situations where we may want an individual to learn something quite important to them. The original arousal concept, referred to in the early chapters as the Yerkes-Dodson Law, originally focused on optimising arousal for learning. Good arousal regulation strategies can lead to 'windows for learning'. The less stressed we are, the more efficient our information processing (Kahneman, 2011). I wish to stress that there are a wide range of therapeutic approaches which can be useful provided they have, at their centre, a therapist who wishes to develop a positive working relationship with the person. In my career, I have been trained in a wide range of different approaches, and for me, any approach which has a central idea that behaviours are simple, or that they are all learned, is by definition over-simplistic. I accept that it is a personal view, but it is always important to resist the urge to over-simplify situations. We are often working with individuals who are highly stressed and traumatised, and the harsh reality is that recovery will always take time. One of the most frustrating elements of this work is that changing people takes considerable time. Therefore, rather than focusing on changing behaviours, our working relationships with people should always be the central focus.

THE REFLECTIVE JOURNEY
Changing Behaviours Requires Positive Relationships

To effect any kind of meaningful change, a working relationship is nearly always essential. A useful way to think about our relationships with distressed individuals or situations is that we are attempting to persuade rather than force people to change an idea. The cognitive psychologist Howard Gardner argued that 'changing minds' requires a whole range of different processes (Gardner, 2004). An essential part of that process is the relationship you have with the person who is providing you with the information to make a decision. If you are unwell, you will consult a doctor, and in general you will trust their advice and opinion.

Even if an individual appears to trust you, it is still quite difficult to develop a good working relationship with someone who is highly distressed. If we consider the knowledge gained by therapists who attempt change, it can be seen that relationships are crucial to all of these processes. There are many debates about the effectiveness of a variety of therapies for adults and children with a range of mental health issues. Debates rage about specific therapies such as cognitive behavioural therapy (CBT), various psychotherapies, and behavioural-based approaches. Whilst there will be merits of specific therapies, research examined in meta-studies have demonstrated that the relationship between the therapist and the client is the most significant factor in determining the success of a therapy (Roth and Fonagy, 2006). Building relationships is another central theme, but it is important to remember that relationship-building can take time. Consider your own relationships that are very important to you. They can deepen or become a little more shallow over time. You have to work at these relationships. The same applies when trying to develop

295

a relationship with an individual who can be challenging or even hostile and confrontational towards you.

'It Takes Two to Argue'

It is the nature of human interaction that arguments between people will nearly always take place. Arguments can often persist and lead to 'unresolved issues'. Observing arguments can also have negative impacts on people. A recent UK report highlighted the impact of parental arguments on the future behaviour of young children, who are 30% more likely to develop behavioural issues (Harold et al., 2016). Resolving arguments requires an individual to make a clear decision to stop engaging in what they are doing, and as low arousal practitioners, this is our role. A constant theme in this book has been that we often inadvertently trigger behaviours. People sometimes struggle to understand that behaviours do not occur in a vacuum. When we interact with people, it is a dynamic 'two way' process. People regularly struggle to see the perspective of other people. Indeed, many national conflicts and wars are often an example of two sides not listening to each other. The reader is encouraged to take a few moments to reflect on a persistent unresolved argument that they may have had with a friend, family member or person they support. How will this argument ever be resolved? When applying a low arousal approach, we may often be expected to be the person to back down, sometimes without even receiving any form of recompense or apology. This is an extremely emotionally difficult process, and it does require you to be highly reflective and forgiving.

This is an easy to statement to make, but in reality, it can be difficult to achieve in day-to-day practice. In our work, it is hard not to be influenced by the diagnostic labels that people attract. Expressions such as personality disorder, schizophrenia, and autism all have connotations that can evoke powerful stereotypes. In addition, when a person is distressed and 'hurling abuse' at you, it is quite easy to view them as aggressive or violent without any deeper reflection. This process becomes even harder if the person has a condition which they do not appear to want to change or alter. Take the example of Henry:

'Henry was a fifty-two-year-old man who had been a problem drinker since the age of nineteen. Despite various attempts by his family over the years to change this situation, Henry's drinking

nearly always returned to its high baselines. Henry would spend months not communicating with family members. He would steal from them, and, when drunk, become extremely abusive. Periods where he was without alcohol would lead to increased agitation and irritability with people. Nobody gave up on Henry, but as the years progressed, it became more and more difficult to view him as anything more than a 'useless drunk'. Eventually, Henry was overwhelmed by the health issues that had accumulated in relation to his drinking, and he sadly passed away. His mother very movingly pointed out that, although times were difficult, she would always see the person first, and the wonderful baby boy that she had raised.'

The reputations that people have can also lead to difficulties in building relationships. A person may be labelled as violent and aggressive by complete strangers. Even the environments that people live in can evoke powerful emotional responses and have an impact on other people's perceptions. I first encountered people with mental illnesses as an undergraduate psychologist spending a series of afternoons on a locked psychiatric ward. The image of people sitting and smoking and not interacting that much at all made it quite a frightening place. One person was introduced to me by a member of staff as 'a violent schizophrenic'. I was even more concerned when that same member of staff told me that this person would be my focus for the next ten weeks of visits. I managed to establish a limited relationship that revolved around cups of tea and playing snooker. On one occasion, I noticed that the gentleman was giving himself two points for a red ball (the real value is one point), and I pointed this out to him. He then threatened me with the snooker cue, and we resolved it very simply by agreeing that all reds would now be valued at two points!

Accept People For Who They Are

Acceptance is a difficult thing, and it is challenging to resist the urge to 'fix' someone when we perceive some kind of 'problem'. Human beings naturally want to help people to change, but this starts with accepting a person as they are. In the therapy field, there is a tendency for professionals to be so solution-focused that they forget they are not trying to repair an object or fix a car. The autistic campaigner Jim Sinclair made it very clear in his early writings that people need to stop seeing people with autism as damaged or broken versions of themselves (1992). In mental health settings, we will often refer to people as being 'in recovery', as though they have some kind of disease or affliction that needs to be fixed. Restoring does not always mean repairing a person. The best analogy for this comes from the arts. You go to an art gallery which contains many different sculptures that represent the diversity of artists and their cultures. Imagine that some of the sculptures are damaged, such as Rodin's 'The Thinker' (1902). This famous image is missing an arm. It would be simply unthinkable to suggest repairing this sculpture in order to improve it. Acceptance is a very difficult part of the journey, but a necessary one.

Take Positive Risks

The more frightened and scared we become, the fewer risks we take with individuals. Risk assessment is important, but if we do not take measured and calculated risks with individuals, then a vicious circle of isolation will ensue. In addition, our goals and objectives for people become more and more limited. I have observed that individuals who display risky behaviours can often end up in both medium and secure environments. Getting into these facilities is much easier than getting out of them. In these circumstances, creating positive risk-taking windows needs to become custom and practice.

Studies appear to suggest that our brains are 'hard-wired' to focus on risks and perceived threats, as this has powerful evolutionary value (Harari, 2011). In addition, we are often cautious when taking risks. In developmental psychology, we know that young children are more risk-averse, trying to understand a world which is slightly alien and frightening to them. Similarly, if we are placed in an unfamiliar environment, our hard-wiring will inevitably make us more cautious in these situations.

It is inevitable that we must take calculated risks. However, according to Nobel Prize winning psychologist Daniel Kahneman, our brains sometimes lead us to over and underestimate risk (2011). In situations where risks are difficult to evaluate, we will generally tend to be cautious. We have many biases hard-wired into our systems, and one of those is to overestimate risks even when data might suggest that a risk is relatively low. Think about an individual who is mugged (leaving them not physically but emotionally harmed) for the first time in their life. Even if they are told that the area that the mugging took place in has a low crime rate and that the chances of being mugged again are very low, who could blame that person for being cautious? They may take many safety measures before they go out into their local community again, even though the statistical risk is probably low. Evaluating risk means also challenging our own biases and beliefs. We also are aware that we may evaluate a risk based on information that is powerful and available to us. The growing research knowledge about our own cognitive biases consistently indicates that we will overestimate some risks and underestimate others.

With adults, it is really important that we encourage them to experiment with new experiences, especially in the later years of their lives. There is an argument that our society has developed a culture of risk management and assessment that actually make it difficult to take risks. Every day we are exposed to managed risks. We fly on airplanes or drive cars knowing that there is a chance that we could be injured or even lose our lives. We try to minimise the risk by making these forms of transport safer, but the reality is that we cannot eradicate all risk. Some risks are not even 'foreseeable'.

When working with highly challenging situations, we may be exposed to physical aggression, self-harm, and may witness things that can lead to trauma, for ourselves and others. The reader should consider that a completely minimised, risk-free life is probably associated with intense boredom, social isolation and most likely unhappiness. If we are working with distressed individuals, we need to create meaningful, happy and engaged lives for them, even if these are short-term and momentary in nature.

When we are supporting people who are highly distressed, if our response is to isolate them in specialised environments or prisons, we may minimise the risk of harm to others whilst reinforcing to that individual a sense of hopelessness. Any positive approach to behaviours of concern must include an element of positive risk-taking. If you are a true practitioner of the low arousal approach, you will be a positive risk-taker, curious to find out what would happen if you do X or Y with a person.

Arguments and debates about the use of punishment will always persist. It is interesting that people often tend to adopt a scale for punishment – smacking your child 'gently' is considered to be different from using excessive force. Sitting a young person on the 'naughty step' may give you a momentary sense of control, but it is not sustainable. The reality is that when we use punishments, we make them acceptable, and those children are very likely to grow up to be adults who use the same strategies.

Punishments are often attractive because they appear to have a rapid impact on people's behaviour. Sadly, years of laboratory psychological research demonstrates that these effects are usually short-term. Animal studies demonstrate that excessive use of punishment, such as electric shock, can lead to a phenomenon known as 'elicited aggression' (Seligman, 1968). That is, they become aggressive when exposed to excessive force. Extreme situations make very poor arguments, but if we are to minimise the use of punishment across the board, then it starts with avoiding smacking children or imposing too many sanctions on adults, which often we have no legal basis to be doing.

Psychologist Ross Greene argues that the key to working with young people is to negotiate rather than impose boundaries (1998). It is often a good approach to identify a problem situation with a person and ask them, 'How can we figure out a way forward?' Negotiation is better, but it is certainly not the easy route. Negotiating can often be considered to be a sign of weakness, but in truth the most effective and humane way to deal with issues is always to talk.

Similarly, the humanist David Pitonyak has illustrated that rather than giving people boundaries, we should give them choices (2005). Negotiation is central to such approaches, but we also know that negotiation requires us to try to understand the perspective of others. This entails a sense of empathy, and the ability to consider another person's perspective. We create rules for a variety of different reasons. There are clear side effects to creating too many aversive rules, such that every time you create a rule, there is an inevitable consequence that will follow if it is broken. Whilst the majority of people try to stick to rules, many do not. If you think about it, we have a sliding scale when interpreting rules. This can range from cheating in a minor classroom test to driving whilst under the influence of alcohol. The latter may be seen as shameful and irresponsible, due to potentially having a huge impact on other people, whereas the former is not.

When we impose too many rules, this inevitably leads to increased stress and, in some cases, resistance and hostility. In many large, group-based, secure settings in adult mental health, we can often witness highly stressed and traumatised people. Often in these situations, staff try to establish control by creating lots of rules. These rules are in actuality points of confrontation. The low arousal approach focuses on minimising rules in order to limit potential conflicts. You can have some boundaries and rules, but always consider who is imposing them

Negotiation is always preferred as an option when adopting the low arousal approach. If you work in a care context, the person who negotiates has to have a good rapport with that individual. In some situations, it is good to have a 'plan negotiator' who is viewed as being outside of the system.

It is not always easy to forgive people, especially if you have been in receipt of intense verbal or physical aggression. It is important to stress that this is a general humanistic message rather than a rigid viewpoint. It is really difficult to forgive someone if they have caused you some form of physical or emotional harm. There are also times where forgiveness may be impossible. I remember a member of staff (sadly now deceased) who did not agree with the forgiving element of the low arousal approach. He argued that forgiveness nearly always led to situations where people learned to dominate others. His main criticism of the low arousal approach was that 'anyone can reduce behaviours if you let people walk all over you'. The concept of bullying is an interesting one. Thomas Hughes, in his classic Victorian novel *Tom Brown's School Days,* describes a central character who is constantly physically and emotionally abused in his private residential school (1857). He is systematically bullied, but ultimately turns the tables on his bullies. Do we stand up to the bully like Tom Brown? Or do we avoid the bully and let them continue in a predatory manner? The problem with these types of examples is that they present simple solutions to complex situations. No person is expected to be a 'doormat' and let people wipe their feet on them. Similarly, how can we expect people to be almost universally forgiving in their work? To be more forgiving, a person must be confident in their own view of the world. The Tom Brown analogy is a useful one as it describes a young man who, despite exposure to such abuse, eventually finds his own humanity. When applying the low arousal approach, we must try to avoid the 'emotional baggage' that often follows from extremely stressful situations. In essence, we are asking people to find their humanity, and, where possible, forgive someone for what they might have done.

People Do Not Have a Plan to Hurt You

I have often found that when you are being exposed to a high level of abuse, it is inevitable that you will begin to feel like a person is doing things on purpose or, in extreme situations, that they are 'targeting' you. The phrase 'they know exactly what they're doing' should be a red flag to any low arousal practitioner. This type of thinking is almost certainly emotion-driven in nature, and typified by fast, almost unconscious processing. The golden rule to the low arousal approach is to recognise when you begin to feel threatened and start to believe that the person you are working with is becoming more and more pre-meditated in their actions. System 2 (slow and logical) thinking is often the solution to this problem. When a situation like this arises, ask yourself the following questions:

1) How do I know that the person is deliberately targeting me?

2) What evidence do I have that the person has planned what they do?

3) How stressed and traumatised is this person?

4) How stressed and traumatised am I?

5) Are there examples of this person melting down or doing things in an unplanned, moment-by-moment manner?

Positive psychologist Professor Martin Seligman, from the University of Pennsylvania, has become a leading figure in the area of positive psychology. Seligman (2011) argues that happiness is a complicated thing, and that there are many forms of happiness. I myself have particularly struggled with the North American, stereotypical view of happiness. This conjures up images of ecstatically smiling people who use phrases like, 'Good job!' and, 'High five!' This is an obvious stereotype, and not one that is reflective of most people's experience of happiness.

Most people benefit from moments of happiness in their lives. If the word 'happiness' causes you concern, then consider other definitions, such as 'the pleasant life'. Low arousal practitioners are often people who are highly sociable as well as effective communicators, seeking out moments of happiness both in themselves and in others. Happiness and other positive emotions can be as contagious as fear and anger.

It is best to think of happiness as moments rather than a constant state. This may appear to be a very obvious point, but positive experiences, moments of happiness and fun are contagious emotions. The American Doctor 'Patch' Adams was well known for trying to use humour to support young children with illnesses. The impact of such an approach is clear. Whilst it is true that humour alone cannot necessarily change a situation, the experience of positive emotions such as happiness and fun are an essential part of our lives, and can bring a greater sense of well-being to a person's life:

'Pavel is a forty-four-year-old man who has spent a great deal of his adult life in a revolving door of psychiatric services and attempts to live in community settings. Apart from his numerous diagnoses, which include a Schizoid Personality Disorder, his main coping strategy is the use of a whole variety of over-the-counter prescription medications in the form of painkillers, as well as abuse of alcohol. People who support Pavel consistently notice that he has a 'great sense of humour'. Even at the lowest points in his life, Pavel is capable of intense humour. The key to working with him was to foster this humour. Often, humorous episodes would be followed by periods of openness which allowed Pavel to reflect on his life. After many attempts to live an engaged and meaningful life in the community, Pavel has finally achieved this.'

Humour can be a coping strategy for highly stressed supporters and distressed individuals alike.

Be Optimistic and Positive in Your Work

Positive and optimistic approaches can provide hope for people (Seligman, 2011). You will have established by now whether you are a 'glass half empty' or 'half full' type of person. Being positive does not mean being cavalier with risk and considered delusional by your friends and colleagues. There are two certainties in life; first, that one day we will all die, and second, that as long as we live, we will continue to grow and develop, often in the face of adversity. Recent studies suggest that by overcoming challenges we become more resilient. Whilst the biological mechanisms are poorly understood, there is evidence that positive emotions and feelings of purpose and meaning in life, as well as physical health (amongst other things) have benefits in terms of increasing one's global mental health (Snidjers et al., 2018).

In crisis management situations, do not let an intense or scary experience determine how you work with people. Be a positive role model. This requires an optimistic outlook to situations. Very recently, my colleagues at Studio3 and I have been working to support a staff team managing a highly distressed adolescent with autism. Her previous years involved being locked in a facility with high levels of staffing and routines, alongside daily use of restraint. A constant question by staff who were adopting the low arousal approach was, 'Are things going to improve?' Based on many years of experience, the simple answer is yes. However, it is challenging to maintain an optimistic approach when you are focused on 'riding out the storm'.

We Are All Allowed to Have Good and Bad Days

I have found that an over-analysis of people's behaviours can have a number of negative side effects. Most notably, we can create a situation where bad experiences or 'bad days' totally impact our judgements about an individual. As practitioners of the low arousal approach, it is essential that we encourage people not to overestimate the impact of bad days. In your own life, think about the number of days that you may have had off sick, or have felt not great. Would you like to be judged based solely on these days when you didn't feel 100% yourself? Now let us consider whether the people we support are really allowed to have 'bad days'. Sadly, the answer is that they are probably not. I was once speaking to a care manager of a progressive organisation who told me very clearly that, in her supported living schemes, a person had to be 'really sick' to have time off (In my opinion, many 'one off' behaviours are related to people being unwell).

When we are supporting highly stressed people, we sometimes minimise the emotional impact that this has on us. Taking a break from a person, even for a few hours or days, should not be considered to be negative. In addition, we emotionally bring our home lives into our work, and this can mean that we can unintentionally communicate strong negative emotions to an individual who is already distressed. In my experience, this negative transaction occurs much more frequently than you would think. Even if you cannot fully control your own emotional state when supporting someone, accepting that it is a factor in any situation is vital. Consider the following example:

'Eleanor supports a number of young women in a specialist eating disorders service. She is an excellent member of staff who often 'tunes in' to the needs of the individuals she supports. On one particularly bad day, Eleanor was involved in multiple incidents, ranging from self-harm to breaking up a fight between two people. Upon reflection, she told her supervisor that the 'perfect storm' of events from that day was also influenced by emotional turmoil within her own family. Her supervisor non-judgementally praised her honesty, and told her, "We are all entitled to have a bad day". This led to increased reflective practice work from Eleanor.'

We also know that our brains suffer from a process known as confirmation bias. If we have had a really difficult day with a distressed person, it is almost certain that we will start to view this as evidence that their behaviour is becoming worse. It is also interesting that people do not appear to consider 'good days' with the same significance. Catastrophising is a dangerous process, and the language we use can actually reinforce negative thoughts. How often have you heard people say that a person's behaviour is only good because they're experiencing a 'honeymoon period'? I often encounter this phrase when supporting staff teams to develop supports for highly distressed individuals who may have previously come from secure environments. Another dangerous phrase which is used is that a behaviour is 'cyclical'. To a certain degree, nearly all of our behaviours are cyclical. When this term is used in the context of behaviours of concern, it implies that, regardless of whether a behaviour appears to improve, the individual will eventually return back to their old behaviour. This is an extremely negative and unhelpful view to have and share amongst staff teams.

Be a Positive Leader and a Role Model

Leaders are not perfect, but they can encourage and nurture talent. My colleague Roy Deveau, a researcher in the intellectual disabilities field, has often pointed out that restrictive practices frequently occur in environments where there is poor leadership. His personal experiences have led him to explore the role of leadership in reducing restrictive practices. Leaders provide emotional as well as practical support for people, and it is essential that they are highly visible, connected to the staff teams and families that they support, and that they routinely provide coaching and feedback (Deveau and Leitch, 2018).

Low arousal practitioners must be able to 'walk the walk', meaning that they must be visible in a crisis and lead from the front. Inevitably, they must not be viewed as experts in the traditional sense of the word. Encouraging a can-do, evidence-based approach to practice is a characteristic that they all share. This does not make people fearless; it is simply about role modelling confidence in these situations. The Studio3 organisation will routinely send individuals into crisis situations, and often it is the case that a fellow practitioner who is willing to work alongside them makes a huge difference to their emotional state. I have often been asked why the Train the Trainers programme at Studio3 is so long. The simple answer is that we are attempting to produce not just teachers but practice leaders. Or, as a colleague said to me recently, 'We don't do death by powerpoint'. There is a strong emphasis on coaching, not just training. In fact, for most of the approaches to supporting people who are highly distressed, positive practice leadership and coaching are nearly always required.

The crisis interventions described above should only be the beginning of an intervention. The next stage often involves increasing demands after a cooling off period. The low arousal approach stresses the importance of the role of psychological trauma, which may lead to panic and anxiety in individuals for care environments.

I should stress that practitioners of the low arousal approach are not 'anti-therapy' in nature. However, our emphasis on short-term crisis management may lead people to think that we do not believe in behaviour change strategies. This is not the case. As a young practitioner trained in behaviour psychology, I truly believed that I had the technology to change most behaviours. I realise now that this approach was somewhat naïve. This has also had a strong influence on my views of everything, from psychotherapy to so-called Positive Behaviour Supports (PBS). In many cases, it is not the approach that I have an issue with, but the application. To put it simply, the approach has to fit the individual, rather than the other way around.

I once worked with an eminent psychologist who told me that he could 'sort out most anxiety problems using Cognitive Behaviour Therapy (CBT) within six, hour-long, weekly sessions'. I do accept that this person was an accomplished therapist, but his success rates were simply not that high. His approach was very technique-oriented, and seemed to lack emotional sensitivity and empathy. I once accompanied him to what was described as a 'crisis referral', visiting a young woman who had attempted an overdose. This psychologist repeatedly told her, "I understand". In supervision later that day, I challenged him gently about his use of this phrase, which led to a fairly heated argument. I accept that this is not true of all therapists, however the use of technique-oriented approaches can sometimes ignore the power of building therapeutic relationships.

There is also a societal obsession with what I would describe as 'trendy' therapies or approaches. Recently, there has been an outpouring of Mindfulness-based approaches. If you examine a range of scientific journals that focus on therapy, you could almost be excused for believing that Mindfulness is the solution for every single problem that a person can have. In my own experience, the 1990s was the period when PBS was portrayed as vital to working with anyone who presented with something we then referred to as 'challenging behaviours'. We have also experienced a CBT revolution over the last 30 years. I wish to distinguish between being sceptical about the universality of these approaches and their effectiveness in practice. As a low arousal practitioner, I acknowledge that these types of approaches have their place. A major key factor in their effectiveness, however, is once again the relationship between therapist and client (Roth and Fonagy, 2006).

Our approach helps to create 'windows of opportunity'. This is achieved by creating positive relationships, even in the most stressful situations. Once this opportunity arises, there needs to be strong consideration for more pro-active approaches to supporting people with their stress and trauma. There are many therapeutic approaches (CBT, PBS, Mindfulness, psychotherapy) that may help an individual and their supporters. The key, for me, is to select the approaches which work best for that individuals. In a broader context, sometimes the distressed person is not the only one who may benefit from these kinds of supports. Sometimes, the supporters of these individuals themselves also require some form of therapeutic engagement.

Many of the people I have supported in my career have been exposed to highly stressful and traumatic life events. Resisting the urge to 'fix' people has created many paradoxical situations for me personally. That is to say, of course I have experienced the desire to make things better for individuals. This desire conflicts with the reality that, for some of the people I have supported, creating a safe, restriction-free world has been a very important goal in its own right. The simple analogy I would give is that there is no point in redecorating your home whilst it is on fire. The low arousal practitioner always wants to put out the fire first, and make the home safe to inhabit before committing to an act of rebuilding or making changes to the environment.

So, are we in favour of therapeutic interventions? The simple answer is that nearly every person-centred, proactive approach is compatible with the low arousal approach. This approach represents a values-based reactive approach to the management of behaviours of concern.

Behaviour is About Us, Not Them

My final comment for the readers of this book is if that we are a part of the problem in crisis management, then that also means that we are part of the solution. It is *our* behaviour which often needs to be altered. We need to understand that one person's distressed behaviour is another person's cry for help. We must constantly question and reflect on our own contribution to stressful situations. In essence, we must start to further understand that behaviour is about perception.

THE REFLECTIVE JOURNEY

The approaches described in these pages are really about changing our focus as practitioners. If a behaviour is going to change, then it has to start with us. If you have worked through all the exercises in this book, or even just selected key chapters, it is my hope that you will have increased your own personal understanding of the low arousal approach. If I have a key word of advice, it is to try not to be a perfectionist, and to accept that sometimes you will get things wrong. The most important thing is to try to improve your approach to supporting individuals by being a reflective practitioner, maintaining positive relationships with the people you support, and being an empathic listener. I hope that you have been encouraged to continue on your own reflective journey as a low arousal practitioner.

REFERENCES

Foreword References:

Elvén, B. H. (2010). *No Fighting, No Biting, No Screaming: How to Make Behaving Positively Possible for People with Autism and Other Developmental Disabilities.* London: Jessica Kingsley Publishers.

McDonnell, A. (2010). *Managing Aggressive Behaviour in Care Settings: Understanding and Applying Low Arousal Approaches.* Oxford: Wiley-Blackwell.

McDonnell, A., McEvoy, J. & Dearden, R. L. (1994). Coping With Violent Situations in the Caring Environment. In T. Wykes (Ed.), *Violence and Health Care Professionals* (pp.189-206). Boston: Springer.

Woodcock, L. & Page A. (2009). *Manging Family Meltdown: The Low Arousal Approach and Autism.* London: Jessica Kingsley Publishers.

Chapter One References:

Bandura, A. (1977). *Social Learning Theory*. Englewood Cliffs, NJ: Prentice Hall.

Bray, G. A., Heisel, W. E., Ashkan, A., Jensen, M. D., Dietz, W. H., Long, M., Kushner, R. F., Daniels, S. R., Wadden, T.A., Tsai, A. G., Hu, F. B., Jakicic, J. M., Ryan, D. H., Wolfe, B. M., & Inge, T. H. (2018). The Science of Obesity Management: An Endocrine Society Scientific Statement. *Endocrine Reviews,* 39(2), 79-132.

Carr, E. G. (1994). Emerging Themes in the Functional Analysis of Problem Behaviour. *Journal of Applied Behaviour Analysis,* 27(2), 393-399.

Durso, G. R. O., Luttrell, A. & Way, B. M. (2015). Over-the-Counter Relief From Pains and Pleasures Alike: Acetaminophen Blunts Evaluation Sensitivity to Both Negative and Positive Stimuli. *Psychological Science,* 26(6), 750-758.

Elvén, B. H. (2010). No Fighting, No Biting, No Screaming: How to Make Behaving Positively Possible for People with Autism and Other Developmental Disabilities. London: Jessica Kingsley Publishers

Emerson, E. (1995). *Challenging Behaviour: Analysis and Intervention in People with Severe Intellectual Disabilities*. Cambridge: Cambridge University Press.

Greene, R. (1998). *The Explosive Child*. New York: Harper Collins.

Kahneman, D. (2011). *Thinking, Fast and Slow*. New York: Farrar, Straus and Giroux.

Lazarus, R. & Folkman, S. (1984). *Stress, Appraisal and Coping*. New York: Springer Publishing.

Marmot, M. (2017, July 18th). Marmot Indicators 2017 – Institute of Health Equity Briefing. *UCL Institute of Health Equity*. Retrieved from http://www.instituteofhealthequity.org/resources-reports/marmot-indicators-2017-institute-of-health-equity-briefing/marmot-indicators-briefing-2017-updated.pdf

McDonnell, A. (2010). *Managing Aggressive Behaviour in Care Settings: Understanding and Applying Low Arousal Approaches.* Oxford: Wiley-Blackwell

McDonnell, A. & Anker, R. (2009). Behaviour Management Versus Behaviour Change: A Useful Distinction? *British Journal of Developmental Disabilities*, 55(2), 157-167.

Milton, D. E. (2012). On the Ontological Status of Autism: The 'Double Empathy Problem'. *Disability & Society,* 27(6), 883-887.

Mischkowski, D., Crocker, J. & Way, B. M. (2016). From Painkiller to Empathy Killer: Acetaminophen (Paracetamol) Reduces Empathy for Pain. *Social Cognitive and Affective Neuroscience*, 11(9), 1345-1353.

Rippon, D., McDonnell, A., Smith, M. A., McCreadie, M. & Wetherell, M. A. (2019). The Development of a Theoretical Framework Concerning the Causes of and Protective Factors Against Work-Related Stress in the Management of Behaviours That Challenge. *Manuscript in preparation.*

Schachter, S. & Singer, J. (1962). Cognitive, Social and Physiological Determinants of Emotional State. *Psychological Review*, 69(5), 379-399.

Schopler, E. & Mesibov, G. (1994). *Behavioural Issues in Autism.* New York: Plenum Press.

Seligman, M. (2011). *Flourish*. Australia: Penguin Random House.

Seligman, M. E., Maier, S. F., & Geer, J. H. (1968). Alleviation of Learned Helplessness in the Dog. *Journal of Abnormal Psychology*, 73(3), 256-262.

Park, D.C. & Festini, S.B. (2017). Theories of Memory and Aging: A Look at the Past and a Glimpse of the Future. *The Journals of Gerontology: Series B, Psychological Sciences and Social Sciences,* 72(1), 82-90.

Pitonyak, D. (2005). 10 Things You Can Do to Support A Person With Difficult Behaviours. *Dimagine,* 1-6. [Internet] Virginia, Available from:<http://www.dimagine.com/> [Accessed 8 July 2009]

Yaribeygi, H., Panahi, Y., Sahraei, H., Johnston, T. P. & Sahebkar, A. (2017). The Impact of Stress on Body Function: A Review. *Experimental and Clinical Services Journal*, 16, 1057-1072.

Chapter Two References:

Benson, H. & Klipper, M. Z. (1975). *The Relaxation Response.* New York: HarperCollins.

Corbett, B. A., Schupp, C. W., Levine, S. & Mendoza, S. (2009). Comparing Cortisol, Stress, and Sensory Sensitivity in Children With Autism. *Autism Research,* 2, 39–49.

Jacobson, E. (1929). *Progressive Relaxation: A Physiological and Clinical Investigation of Muscular States and Their Significance in Psychology and Medical Practice.* Chicago: University of Chicago

Lazarus, R. S. & Folkman, S. (1980). An Analysis of Coping in a Middle Aged Community Sample. *Journal of Health and Social Behavior,* 21, 219-239.

Lazarus, R. S. & Folkman, S. (1984). *Stress, Appraisal, and Coping.* New York: Springer.

Singh, N. N., Lancioni, G. E., Winton, A. Fisher, B. C., Wahler, R.G., Mcaleavey, K., Singh, J. & Sabaawi, M. (2006). Mindful Parenting Decreases Aggression, Noncompliance, and Self-Injury in Children with Autism. *Journal of Emotional and Behavioural Disorders,* 14(3), 169-177.

Chapter Three References:

American Psychiatric Association. (2013). *Diagnostic and Statistical Manual of Mental Disorders* (5th ed.). Washington, DC: Author.

Cohen, J. A., Deblinger, E., Mannarino, A. P., & Steer, R. A. (2004). A Multisite, Randomized Controlled Trial for Children with Sexual Abuse–Related PTSD Symptoms. *Journal of the American Academy of Child & Adolescent Psychiatry*, 43 (4), 393-402.

Hughes, D. A., Golding, K. S. & Hudson, J. (2019). *Healing Relational Trauma with Attachment-Focused Interventions: Dyadic Developmental Psychotherapy with Children and Families.* New York: W.W Norton & Company Ltd.

McDonnell, A. (2010). *Managing Aggressive Behaviour in Care Settings: Understanding and Applying Low Arousal Approaches.* Oxford: Wiley-Blackwell.

Mevissen, L., De Jongh, A., Lievegoed, R. & Seubert, A. (2011). Do Persons with Intellectual Disability and Limited Verbal Capacities Respond to Trauma Treatment? *Journal of Intellectual and Developmental Disability,* 36 (4), 274-9.

Chapter Four References:

Baron-Cohen, S. & Wheelwright, S. (2004). The Empathy Quotient: An Investigation of Adults with Asperger Syndrome or High Functioning Autism, and Normal Sex Differences. *Journal of Autism and Developmental Disorders*, 34(2), 163-175.

Coll, M. P., Viding, E., Rütgen, M., Silani, G., Lamm, C., Catmur, C., & Bird, G. (2017). Are We Really Measuring Empathy? Proposal for a New Measurement Framework. *Neuroscience & Biobehavioural Reviews*, 83, 132-139.

Cuff, B. M. P., Brown, S. J., Taylor, L. & Howat, D. J. (2016). Empathy: A Review of the Concept. *Emotion Review*, 8(2), 144-153.

Decety, J. & Jackson, P. L. (2004). The Functional Architecture of Human Empathy. *Behavioural and Cognitive Neuroscience Reviews*, 3(2), 71-100.

De Waal, F. B. M. (2008). Putting the Altruism Back into Altruism: The Evolution of Empathy. *Annual Review of Psychology*, 59, 279-300.

De Vignemont, F. & Singer, T. (2006). The Empathic Brain: How, When and Why? *Trends in Cognitive Sceinces,* 10(10), 435-441.

Milton, D. E. (2017). *A Mismatch of Salience: Explorations of the Nature of Autism from Theory to Practice.* East Sussex: Pavilion Publishing and Media Ltd.

Spreng, R.N., McKinnon, M.C., Mar, R.A., & Levine, B. (2009). The Toronto Empathy Questionnaire: Scale Development and Initial validation of a factor-analytic solution to multiple empathy measures. *Journal of Personality Assessment,* 91(1): 62-71.

Zaki, J. & Ochsner, K. N. (2012). The Neuroscience of Empathy: Progress, Pitfalls and Promise. *Nature Neuroscience*, 15(5), 675-680

Chapter Five References:

Cannon, W, B. (1929). *Bodily Changes in Pain, Hunger, Fear and Rage* (2nd Ed.). New York: Plenum.

Chambless, D. L. & Gracely, E. J. (1989). Fear of Fear and the Anxiety Disorders. *Cognitive Therapy and Research*, 13(1), 9-20.

Elvén, B. H. (2010). *No Fighting, No Biting, No Screaming: How to Make Behaving Positively Possible for People with Autism and Other Developmental Disabilities*. London: Jessica Kingsley Publishers.

Gray, J. A. (1998). *The Psychology of Fear and Stress* (2nd Ed.). New York: Cambridge University Press.

Harari, Y. N. (2011). *Sapiens: A Brief History of Humankind*. New York: HarperCollins

Kahneman, D. (2011). *Thinking, Fast and Slow*. New York: Farrar, Straus and Giroux.

Novaco, R.W. (1977) 'Stress Inoculation: A Cognitive Therapy for Anger and its Application to a Case of Depression', *Journal of Consulting and Clinical Psychology,* 45(4): 600-8

Sapolsky, R. (2017). *Behave: The Biology of Humans at Our Best and Worst*. London: Penguin.

Seligman, M. E. (1971). Phobias and Preparedness. *Behaviour Therapy*, 2, 307-320.

Wetherell, M. A., Hare, O. A., & Smith, M. A. (2013). State Anxiety and Cortisol Reactivity to Skydiving in Novice Versus Experienced Skydivers. *Physiology & Behaviour*, 118, 40-44.

Chapter Six References:

Clausen, E. I. (2007). *Psychology of Anger*. New York: Nova Science Publishers.

Darley, J. M. & Latané, B. (1968). Bystander Intervention in Emergencies: Diffusion of Responsibility. *Journal of Personality and Social Psychology*, 8, 377-383.

Darley, J. M. & Latane, B. (1970). *The Unresponsive Bystander: Why Doesn't He Help?* New Jersey: Prentice Hall .

Heitler, S. (2018, June). What Are the Options for Kids with an Often-Angry Parent? *Psychology Today*. Retrieved from https://www.psychologytoday.com/us/blog/resolution-not-conflict/201806/what-are-the-options-kids-often-angry-parent

Kahneman, D. (2011). *Thinking, Fast and Slow*. New York: Farrar, Straus and Giroux.

Lundstrom, M., Astrom, S., & Graneheim, U. H. (2007). Caregivers' Experiences of Exposure to Violence in Services for People with Learning Disabilities. *Journal of Psychiatric and Mental Health Nursing*, 14(4), 338-345.

Mind (2018, July) How to Cope with Anger. Retrieved from https://www.mind.org.uk/information-support/types-of-mental-health-problems/anger/managing-outbursts/#TrySomeTechniquesToManageYourFeelings

Novaco, R. W. (2000). Anger. In A. E. Kazdin (Ed.) *Encyclopaedia of Psychology* (pp. 170-174). Washington, DC: American Psychological Association and Oxford University Press.

Rodgers, J.E. (2014, March). Go Forth in Anger. *Psychology Today*. Retrieved   from https://www.psychologytoday.com/gb/articles/201403/go-forth-in-anger

Sapolsky, R. (2017). *Behave: The Biology of Humans at Our Best and Worst*. London: Penguin.

Chapter Seven References:

Dagnan, D., Hull, A., & McDonnell, A. (2013). The Controllability Beliefs Scale Used with Carers of People with Intellectual Disabilities: Psychometric Properties. *Journal of Intellectual Disability Research*, 57(5), 422-428.

Dagnan, D., Grant, F. & McDonnell, A. (2004). Understanding Challenging Behaviour in Older People: The Development of the Controllability Beliefs Scale. *Behavioural and Cognitive Psychotherapy*, 32(4), 501-506.

Danmer, D. D., Snowdon, D. A. & Friesen, W. V. (2001). Positive Emotions in Early Life and Longevity: Findings from the Nun Study. *Journal of Personality and Social Psychology*, 80(5), 804-813.

Ferster, C. B., & Skinner, B. F. (1957). *Schedules of Reinforcement*. East Norwalk: Appleton-Century-Crofts.

Kushlick, A., Trower, P., & Dagnan, D. (1997). Applying Cognitive-Behavioural Approaches to the Carers of People with Learning Disabilites who Display Challenging Behaviour. In Kroese, B. S., Dagnan, D. & Loumidis, K. (Eds) *Cognitive-Behaviour Therapy for People with Learning Disabilities* (pp.141-161). London: Psychology Press.

Marmot, M. (2017, July 18th). Marmot Indicators 2017 – Institute of Health Equity Briefing. *Public Health England, UCL Institute of Health Equity*. Retrieved from http://www.instituteofhealthequity.org/resources-reports/marmot-indicators-2017-institute-of-health-equity-briefing/marmot-indicators-briefing-2017-updated.pdf

Marmot, M.G. (2015). Marmot Indicators 2015 for Local Authorities in England. *Fair Society, Healthy Lives*. Retrieved from http://www.instituteofhealthequity.org/resources-reports/marmot-indicators-2015/marmot-indicators-2015-background-report.pdf

Marmot, M. G., Bosma, H., Hemingway, H., Brunner, E. & Stansfeld, S. (1997). Contribution of Job Control and Other Risk Factors to Social Variations in Coronary Heart Disease Incidence. *The Lancet*, 350(9073), 235-239.

McKenna, G., Cushen, A., McDonnell, A. & McTigue, O. (2015). Polypharmacy Audit: A Practice Review of Polypharmacy in a Congregated Setting Among Intellectual Disability Residents. *Unpublished manuscript.*

Mischel, W. (2014). *The Marshmallow Test: Mastering Self-Control.* New York: Random House.

Pilkington, E. (2018, November). 'It's Torture': Critics Step Up Bid to Stop US School Using Electric Shocks on Children. *The Guardian*, Retrieved from https://www.theguardian.com/us-news/2018/nov/16/judge-rotenberg-center-massachusetts-electric-shocks

Prison Reform Trust. (2018). Prison: The Facts. *Bromley Briefings Summer 2018.* Retrieved from *http://www.prisonreformtrust.org.uk/Portals/0/Documents/Bromley%20Briefings/Summer%202018%20factfile.pdf*

Rippon, D., McDonnell, A., Smith, M. A., McCreadie, M. & Wetherell, M. A. (2019). The Development of a Theoretical Framework Concerning the Causes of and Protective Factors Against Work-Related Stress in the Management of Behaviours That Challenge. *Manuscript in preparation.*

Sturge, G. (2018). UK Prison Population Statistics. *Briefing Paper Number CBP-04334.* Retrieved from https://researchbriefings.parliament.uk/ResearchBriefing/Summary/SN04334#fullreport

Weiner, B. (1980). A Cognitive (Attribution)-Emotion-Action Model of Motivated Behaviour: An Analysis of Judgements of Help-Giving, *Journal of Personality and Social Psychology,* 39(2), 186-200.

Chapter Eight References:

Hayes, S. C., Strosahl, K. & Wilson, K.G. (1999). *Acceptance and Commitment Therapy: An Experiential Approach to Behaviour Change.* New York: Guilford Press.

Keenan, B. (1992). *An Evil Cradling.* New York: Vintage.

Chapter Nine References:

Alghadir, A. H., Gabr, S. A. & Aly, F. A. (2015). The Effects of Four Weeks of Aerobic Training on Saliva Cortisol and Testosterone in Young Healthy Persons. *Journal of Physical Therapy Science*, 27(7), 2029-2033.

Anderson, C. A. & Bushman, B. J. (2002). Human Aggression. *Annual Review of Psychology*, 53, 27−51.

Benson, H. & Klipper, M. Z. (2000). *The Relaxation Response*. New York: HarperTorch.

Bidzan-Bluma, I. & Lipowska, M. (2018). Physical Activity and Cognitive Functioning of Children: A Systematic Review. *International Journal of Environmental Research and Public Health,* 15(4), 800.

Chen, P. Y. & Spector, P. E. (1992). Relationships of Work Stressors with Aggression, Withdrawal, Theft and Substance Abuse: An Exploratory Study. *Journal of Occupational and Organisational Psychology*, 65(3), 177-184.

Csikszentmihalyi, M. (1990). *Flow: The Classic Work on How to Achieve Happiness*. London: Rider.

Groden, J., Cautela, J., Prince, S. & Berryman, J. (1994). The Impact of Stress and Anxiety on Individuals with Autism and Developmental Disabilities. In Schopler, E. & Mesibov, G. B. (Eds.) *Behavioural Issues in Autism* (pp.177-194). Boston: Springer.

Howlin, P. (1998). *Children with Autism and Aspergers Syndrome: A Guide for Practitioners and Carers*. Chichester: Wiley.

James, W. (1884). What is an Emotion? *Mind,* 9(34), 188-205.

Lazarus, R. S. & Folkman, S. (1984). *Stress, Appraisal, and Coping.* New York: Springer.

Linsley, P. (2006).*Violence and Aggression in the Workplace: A Practical Guide for All Healthcare Staff.* Oxford: Radcliffe Publishing.

McCreadie, M. & McDermott, J. (2014). 'Tuning In': Client Practitioner Stress Transactions In Autism. In G. Jones & E. Hurley (Eds.) *GAP: Autism, Happiness and Well-being.* Plymouth: BILD Publications (pp.24-31).

McDonnell, A., McCreadie, M., Mills, R., Deveau, R., Anker, R., & Hayden, J. (2014). The Role of Physiological Arousal in the Management of Challenging Behaviours in Individuals with Autistic Spectrum Disorders. *Research in Developmental Disabilities*, 36, 311-322.

Miller, S. (1995). Monitoring Versus Blunting Styles of Coping with Cancer Influence the Information Patients Want and Need About Their Disease. Implications for Cancer Screening and Management. *Cancer*, 76(2), 167-177.

Niemiec, R. M. (2016). The Mindful Pause: How to Help Others. *Psychology Today.* Retrieved from https://www.psychologytoday.com/gb/blog/what-matters-most/201604/the-mindful-pause-how-help-others

Rippon, D., McDonnell, A., Smith, M. A., McCreadie, M. & Wetherell, M. A. (2019). The Development of a Theoretical Framework Concerning the Causes of and Protective Factors Against Work-Related Stress in the Management of Behaviours That Challenge. *Manuscript in preparation.*

Selye, H. (1976). Stress Without Distress. In Serban, G. (eds.) *Psychopathology of Human Adaptation* (pp.137-146). Boston, MA: Springer.

Selye, H. (1956). *The Stress of Life*. New York: McGraw-Hill.

Shonin, E., Van Gordon, W. & Singh, N. N. (2015). *Buddhist Foundations of Mindfulness*. New York: Springer.

Wetherell, M. A., Hare, O. A., & Smith, M. A. (2013). State Anxiety and Cortisol Reactivity to Skydiving in Novice Versus Experienced Skydivers. *Physiology & Behaviour*, 118, 40-44.

Yerkes, R. M. & Dodson, J. D. (1908). The Relation of Strength of Stimulus to Rapidity of Habit-Formation. *Journal of Comparative Neurology and Psychology*, 18, 459-482.

Chapter Ten References:

Allen, D. & Tynan, H. (2000). Responding to Aggressive Behaviour: Impact of Training on Staff Members' Knowledge and Confidence. *Mental Retardation*, 38(2), 97-104.

Elvén, B. H. (2010). *No Fighting, No Biting, No Screaming: How to Make Behaving Positively Possible for People with Autism and Other Developmental Disabilities.* London: Jessica Kingsley Publishers

Harris, M. and Fallot, R.D. (2001). Envisioning a Trauma-Informed Service System: A Vital Paradigm Shift. *New Directions for Mental Health Services*, 89, 3-22.

Itard, J. G. (1802). *The Wild Boy of Aveyron.* New York: Appleton-Century.

Korczak, J. (1929). *The Child's Right to Respect.* France: Council of Europe Publishing.

McDonnell, A., McCreadie, M., Mills, R., Deveau, R., Anker, R., & Hayden, J. (2014). The Role of Physiological Arousal in the Management of Challenging Behaviours in Individuals with Autistic Spectrum Disorders. *Research in Developmental Disabilities*, 36, 311-322.

McDonnell, A. (2010). *Managing Aggressive Behaviour in Care Settings: Understanding and Applying Low Arousal Approaches.* Oxford: Wiley-Blackwell.

McDonnell, A., Waters, T. & Jones, D. (2002). Low Arousal Approaches in the Management of Challenging Behaviours. In D. Allen (Ed.) *Ethical Approaches to Physical Interventions: Responding to Challenging Behaviours in People with Intellectual Disabilities.* Plymouth: BILD (pp.104 – 113).

McDonnell, A.A., McEvoy, J. & Dearden, R.L. (1994). Coping with Violent Situations in the Caring Environment. In T. Wykes (Ed.) *Violence and Health Care Professionals*. London: Chapman and Hall (pp.189-206).

McDonnell, A., Reeves, S., Johnson, A. & Lane, A. (1998). Managing Challenging Behaviour in an Adult with Learning Disabilities: The Use of the Low Arousal Approach. *Behavioural and Cognitive Psychology*, 26(2), 163-171.

Page, A., McDonnell, A., Gayson, C., Moss, F., Mohammed, N., Smith, C., & Vanes, N. (2015). Clinical Holding with Children Who Display Behaviours that Challenge. *British Journal of Nursing*, 24(21), 1086-1093.

Pitonyak, D. (2005). 10 Things You Can Do to Support A Person With Difficult Behaviours. *Dimagine,* 1-6. [Internet] Virginia, Available from:<http://www.dimagine.com/> [Accessed 8 July 2009]

Rachman, S. (1978). *Fear and Courage*. New York: W. H. Freeman & Co.

Richetin, J. & Richardson, D. S. (2008). Automatic Processes and Individual Differences in Aggressive Behaviour. *Aggression and Violent Behavior*, 13(6), 423-430.

Schon, D. (1987). *Educating the Reflective Practitioner*. San Francisco: Josey Bass.

Watts, D. & Morgan, G. (1994). Malignant Alienation: Dangers for Patients who are Hard to Like. *British Journal of Psychiatry*, 164, 11-15.

Woodcock, L. & Page A. (2010). *Manging Family Meltdown: The Low Arousal Approach and Autism*. London: Jessica Kingsley Publishers.

Chapter Eleven References:

Calhoun, J. B. (1962). Population Density and Social Pathology. *Scientific American,* 206, 139-148.

Candini, M., Giuberti, V., Manattini, A., Grittani, S., di Pellegrino, G. & Frassinetti, F. (2016). Personal Space Regulation in Childhood Autism: Effects of Social Interaction and Person's Perspective. *Autism Research*, 10(1), 144-154.

Darwin, C. (1872). *The Expression of the Emotion of Man in Animals.* London: John Murray.

Kaplan, S. G. & Wheeler, E. G. (1983). Survival Skills for Working with Potentially Violent Clients. *Social Casework,* 64(6), 339-346.

Kinzel, A. F. (1970). Body-Buffer Zone in Violent Prisoners. *American Journal of Psychology*, 127(1), 59-64.

McDonnell, A. (2010). *Managing Aggressive Behaviour in Care Settings: Understanding and Applying Low Arousal Approaches.* Oxford: Wiley-Blackwell.

Sorokowski, P. et al. (2017). Preferred Interpersonal Distances: A Global Comparison, *Journal of Cross-Cultural Psychology*, 48(4), 577-592. Retrieved from https://doi.org/10.1177/0022022117698039

Strauss, B. (2002). Social Facilitation in Motor Tasks: A Review of Research and Theory. *Psychology of Sport and Exercise*, 3(3), 237–256. Retrieved from doi:10.1016/S1469-0292(01)00019-x

Chapter Twelve References:

Lacy, J. W. & Stark, C. E. L. (2013). The Neuroscience of Memory: Implications for the Courtroom. *National Review of Neuroscience*, 14(9), 649-658.

Pitonyak, D. (2005). 10 Things You Can Do to Support A Person With Difficult Behaviours. *Dimagine,* 1-6. [Internet] Virginia, Available from:<http://www.dimagine.com/> [Accessed 8 July 2009]

Rogers, C. R. (1951). *Client-Centred Therapy*. London: Constable & Robinson Ltd.

Chapter Thirteen References:

Beck, A. T. (1976). *Cognitive Therapy and the Emotional Disorders.* London: Penguin.

Berne, E. (1964). *Games People Play: The Psychology of Human Relationships.* New York: Grove Press.

Festinger, L. (1962). *A Theory of Cognitive Dissonance.* Redwood City: Stanford University Press.

Gardner, H. (2004). *Changing Minds: The Art and Science of Changing Our Own and Other People's Minds.* Massachusetts: Harvard Business Review Press.

Korczak, J. (1929). *The Child's Right to Respect.* France: Council of Europe Publishing.

Lovaas, O. I. (1987). Behavioural Treatment and Normal Educational and Intellectual Functioning in Young Autistic Children. *Journal of Consulting and Clinical Psychology,* 55(1), 3-9.

McDonnell, A. & Deveau, R. (2009). As the Last Resort: Reducing the Use of Restrictive Physical Interventions Using Organisational Approaches. *British Journal of Learning Disabilities,* 37(3), 172-177.

Morrison, N. (2014). The Surprising Truth About Discipline in Schools. *Forbes.* Retrieved from https://www.forbes.com/sites/forbes-finds/2019/04/15/sony-x950g-review-an-impressive-tv-that-can-get-very-bright/#783ba5972a5f

Tajfel, H. (1979). Individuals and Groups in Social Psychology. *British Journal of Social and Clinical Psychology,* 18(2), 183-190.

Tzu, S. (5th Century B.C.). *The Art of War*. Online: Pax Librorum.

Walmsley, R. (2018). World Prison Population List. *World Prison Brief* (11th ed.). Retrieved from http://www.prisonstudies.org/sites/default/files/resources/downloads/world_prison_population_list_11th_edition_0.pdf

Chapter Fourteen References:

Deveau, R. & Leitch, S. (2018). Person-Centred Restraint Reduction: Planning and Action. Plymouth: BILD Publications.

Gardner, H. (2004). *Changing Minds: The Art and Science of Changing Our Own and Other People's Minds.* Massachusetts: Harvard Business Review Press.

Greene, R. (1998). *The Explosive Child.* New York: Harper Collins.

Harari, Y. N. (2011). *Sapiens: A Brief History of Humankind.* New York: HarperCollins

Harold, G., Acquah, D., Chowdry, H. & Sellers, R. (2016). What works to enhance interparental relationships and improve outcomes for children? *Early Intervention Foundation.* Retrieved from https://www.eif.org.uk/report/what-works-to-enhance-interparental-relationships-and-improve-outcomes-for-children/

Kahneman, D. (2011). *Thinking, Fast and Slow.* New York: Farrar, Straus and Giroux.

Knightsmith, P. (2018). Can I Tell You About Self-Harm? A Guide for Friends, Family and Professionals. London: Jessica Kingsley Publishers.

Lewis, F., Schaffer, K., Sussex, J., O'Neill, P. & Cockcroft, L. (2014). The Trajectory of Dementia in the UK – Making a Difference. *Office of Health Economics Consulting Report.* Retrieved from https://www.ohe.org/publications/trajectory-dementia-uk-making-difference

Pitonyak, D. (2005). 10 Things You Can Do to Support A Person With Difficult Behaviours. *Dimagine,* pp.1-6. [Internet]

Virginia, Available from:<http://www.dimagine.com/> [Accessed 8 July 2009]

Roth, A. & Fonagy, P. (2006). *What Works for Whom: A Critical Review of Psychotherapy Research.* New York: Guilford Press.

Seligman, M. (2011). *Flourish.* Australia: Penguin Random House.

Seligman, M. E., Maier, S. F., & Geer, J. H. (1968). Alleviation of Learned Helplessness in the Dog. *Journal of Abnormal Psychology*, 73(3), 256-262.

Sinclair, J. (1992). Bridging the Gap: An Inside-Out View of Autism (Or, Do You Know What I Don't Know?). In E. Schopler & G. Mesibov (Eds.) *High-Functioning Individuals with Autism* (pp.1-17). New York: Plenum Press.

Snijders, C., Pries, L. K., Sgammeglia, N., Jowf, G. A., Youssef, N. A., de Nijs, L., Guloksuz, S. & Rutten, B. P. F. (2018). Resilience Against Traumatic Stress: Current Developments and Future Directions. *Frontiers in Psychology,* 9, 676. Retrieved from doi.org/10.3389/fpsyt.2018.00676

Woodcock, L. & Page A. (2009). *Manging Family Meltdown: The Low Arousal Approach and Autism.* London: Jessica Kingsley Publishers.